PRIVILEGED

Experiences From My Unusual 40-Year Career
with One of America's Most Iconic Companies

Jim,
Enjoyed our time together!

Michael A. Davis

PRIVILEGED

Experiences From My Unusual 40-Year Career
with One of America's Most Iconic Companies

Michael A. Davi

Cover photo by Michael A. Davi
Book design by The Troy Book Makers

Printed in the United States of America
The Troy Book Makers • Troy, New York • thetroybookmakers.com

To order additional copies of this title,
contact your favorite local bookstore
or visit www.shoptbmbooks.com

ISBN: 978-1-61468-469-5

Dedicated to the memory of
my dad, Gabriel L. Davi (1929-2005)
and my mom, Melinda G. Davi (1930-2018)
who passed away soon after
I completed the manuscript for this book.

CONTENTS

FORWARD

I TOOK ON THE IMMENSE CHALLENGE of writing this book for several reasons. My main goal is to encourage today's young people to consider science and technology as a career. By documenting the ups and downs of my own unusual and varied career at GE, made possible by the educational opportunities I pursued, I hope to instill a sense of overall optimism—particularly in those who may share my humble background—while highlighting the critical importance of a solid education.

Second, I want to pay tribute to my family. In this book's Prologue, I begin with the story of my immigrant grandparents, all of whom were non-professional employees at GE at some time in their lives. Like many of their fellow immigrants, they struggled with language, culture and a myriad of other issues, yet they persevered. And my own parents, with values shaped by the experience of the prior generation, they set the stage for my opportunities. From this vantage point, my GE career can be thought of as a realization of "The Great American Dream" my grandparents envisioned when they came to this country.

Finally, I must acknowledge my many GE colleagues who contributed to my continual learning process—and my success. I worked with literally thousands of remarkable people from a kaleidoscope of different cultures and ethnicities. This broad exposure gave me a global awareness that would seem almost impossible to find in the confines of a small northeast city.

I've established lifelong friendships with many of my associates, and our shared bond is truly remarkable. Whenever I encounter a former co-worker, the recognition and camaraderie are instantaneous and genuine, as if we were never apart. I still meet with many of my former colleagues regularly to relive past times, discuss current events, and offer each other help and advice.

All people and events described in this book are all real, based upon my memory and first hand experiences. Throughout the book I often used actual names, most with permission, but sometimes chose to maintain a degree of anonymity by just using initials where I thought it would be prudent to do so. In particular, I avoided making specific reference to GE client names as some may not want episodes I discussed in the public domain.

All opinions are my own, except as otherwise noted. Due to realistic space limitations and my own fallible memory, I could not mention most of the thousands of co-workers I encountered in my GE career. So, let me apologize in advance to those co-workers who I couldn't include in this text. Perhaps this book will inspire them to share their experiences, which I expect may be even more interesting and compelling than my own.

Now, on to my story, beginning with the Prologue and my four immigrant grandparents who started it all...

PROLOGUE

FATE AND CIRCUMSTANCE DETERMINE MUCH about the choices and opportunities we all are presented with in life. In my case, being born in the small, yet historic east central New York State town of Schenectady, during the post-World War II baby boom, was strictly chance. Decades earlier, cross currents of fate and time brought my grandparents to the same then-bustling small city during a most fortunate period. Only a few decades before my grandparents' arrival in America, Thomas Edison, the great inventor and entrepreneur, located what was to become the iconic General Electric (GE) Company there.

These were only the first of a remarkable series of incredible coincidences that somehow aligned to guide me to a most rewarding and unusual 40-year career with GE. Perhaps it was my destiny to one day have a professional career and, in a way, bring to fruition the early aspirations of my immigrant grandparents, albeit one in which my experiences far exceeded any expectations that they—or I—could have imagined.

Like so many millions of other immigrants, my grandparents were drawn to this country in search of better lives. Although I have only tiny fragments of their stories, and will never be able to completely understand their perspectives and feelings, it seems fitting to begin my book with them. Certainly their stories—told in their own voice—would be quite spectacular in their own right. Through discussions with family members and my personal research, along with some key assistance from very helpful individuals, I have learned some startling details that present clearer, dramatic and sometimes emotional elements to my own story. It is my privilege to share them with you.

Each of my grandparents was born in a tiny agricultural village in one of three adjacent provinces in the southern Italian state of Campagna. Three of the tiny villages, home to both grandfathers and my maternal grandmother, are in relatively close proximity. Today it would be only about a 20-minute drive between them, but in the late 1800s, travel generally was limited to foot or horse-drawn transport. Hence, even these geographically close villages were fairly isolated from each other and the larger outside world. Given the time and circumstance, it is not surprising, therefore, that none of the four grandparents met in their Italian homeland.

My paternal grandfather and namesake became known in America as Michael Davi, but was baptized in Italy as Michelangelo Iadevaia. He was the first of my four grandparents to arrive. As family lore goes, his mother died very young and when his father, Gabriele, remarried, there were difficulties with his stepmother. In fact, overheard discussions led the family to believe that my grandfather actually suffered physical abuse at the hands of his stepmother.

Before I began my own research for this book, the general family consensus was that Michael came alone to this country at age 16 to escape from this unpleasant family situation. Much to our surprise, I discovered that my Great-grandfather Gabriele (my dad's namesake) actually accompanied young Michael to America. According to the manifest of the SS America, which arrived in New York on April 4, 1910, Gabriele and Michael arrived together[1]. Apparently, Great-grandfather Gabriele accompanied Michael to help get his son settled with relatives already living in Rome, New York. Details about his early years there, other than the fact that he played the French horn in local bands, are very sparse.

After working for several years in Rome, New York, records show that Michael joined the US Army in 1918 to assist in World War I efforts. In doing so, like so many others of that era, he was naturalized as a US citizen as part of his Army induction. Timing was indeed fortunate for him, as the war ended just as he completed his basic Army training. In December of that same year, he was honorably discharged, sparing him the dangers of that terrible conflict.

At some point following his Army discharge Michael apparently learned of employment opportunities in Thomas Edison's fast-growing General

---

1 Prior research had not proven fruitful, but, it appears that a common name spelling error was the reason. As was often the case the Italian surnames were somewhat misspelled. In this case the "I" was inadvertently changed to a "J" along with a slight interchange of letters at the end, resulting in the handwritten name of Jedevia appearing on the manifest. All other information correlates to known birth, hometown and destination knowledge garnered from other independent sources.

Electric plant in nearby Schenectady. Sometime in the early to mid-1920s he relocated to Schenectady. And, while living in a boarding house, my grandfather became acquainted with a single Italian woman, Filomena Caso. In December 1925, he married Filomena, my grandmother.

Also perhaps that year, if not earlier, he was hired at the GE plant in Schenectady, thus becoming the first Michael Davi to work at GE. When you think about it, this was quite an accomplishment. Like many of his fellow immigrants, my grandfather arrived in America with minimal formal education. But, like many others, he possessed a powerful drive and work ethic, coupled with a willingness and ability to learn. Chance and circumstance gave him the opportunity to improve his lot in life. GE was quick to recognize these desirable traits and certainly capitalized on this available immigrant workforce.

During my investigation of family roots, I discovered an unexpected treasure trove in the GE News, an in-house publication for GE's Schenectady workforce. Here, I found the earliest GE documentation of my Grandfather Michael's employment through an article dated September 1925. In fact, his older children are fairly certain he most likely was employed at GE even earlier than this date. Piecing together family lore, GE News articles and references in the Schenectady City Directory, it seems most likely Grandpa Michael worked in what was then the Appliance department of GE as a machine operator. My aunts, uncle and father seem to recall his work involved assembly of the very popular "Monitor Top" refrigerators, which at the time (mid-1920s) was one of GE's most successful products[2]. When learning of this, I couldn't help but smile, because my grandfather was involved with a leading GE product decades before I was born. More than half a century later, I also would work on some of GE's world-class leading gas turbines ... but more about that later in this book.

Now with stable employment, Michael and Filomena began a family. Daughter Mary was born in 1927, and a boy followed about two years later in January 1929. This boy was to become my dad, Gabriel. The Davi family grew steadily with my Aunt Louise and Uncle Sal, followed by two more daughters, who would become my aunts Pauline and Rose, bringing the total number of

---

2 Reference: A Century of Progress, The General Electric Story, GE Hall of History Publication, Volume 3 "On the Shoulders of Giants 1924-1946", p. 12.

children to six. The growing family was reflective of my grandfather's mounting success at GE and the company's overall growth as well. Everything seemed to be playing out as another one of many success stories for another hard-working immigrant family. What could possibly be better than this?

But life took a tragic turn in 1941, as Grandfather Michael became ill with what is, even today, one of the most lethal forms of pancreatic cancer. In January 1942, at the very young age of 46, my grandfather died, leaving my Grandmother Filomena a widow with six children, ages 3 to15. My dad, Gabriel, was the oldest son, at just 13 years of age. This tragedy was compounded by the fact that the US had been drawn into World War II following the Pearl Harbor attack only weeks before. Especially hard hit was my grandmother, who faced tremendous hardship in the weeks, months and years following her husbands' death. The tragedy of my grandfather's sudden death left an indelible mark on the family that impacted everyone in many ways for decades. One such long-term impact of my grandfather's premature death was that it drew focus away from education for the children as the family shifted into "survival mode," forcing the eldest children into the workplace much sooner than planned.

In an eerily similar manner, yet with its own unique twists, parallel events were also at work shaping the maternal side of my family. Just over two years after Michael set foot in America, my maternal grandfather, Antonio Iacobucci, arrived in New York. It was early June 1912, about a month before his 19th birthday. Most likely it was family friends or perhaps some distant relatives that drew him to the New Haven, Connecticut, area, where he would spend the next five years or so working and learning basic skills demanded of so many immigrants trying to assimilate into the rapidly industrializing US. WWI again played a role in shaping family history as my grandfather enlisted in the US Army in 1918 and also was naturalized as a US citizen when he did so. Grandpa Antonio was not as lucky as Grandpa Michael. He was deployed, and fought for the US overseas in France for about nine months. Grandpa never spoke to me about his war experiences, but I believe they had a major impact on him, given stories my mother has shared over the years. Perhaps the war experiences explain some of his drive and temperament. In hindsight, I can imagine some potential impact from post-traumatic stress disorder (PTSD), which was little understood at the time.

Following his honorable discharge from the US Army, in a similar scenario to that of Grandpa Michael, Grandpa Antonio also was drawn to Edison's ever-growing Schenectady GE plant and also found work there. He built upon electrical knowledge acquired while working in the New Haven area. Without question, Schenectady, with its bustling GE plant and the American Locomotive Company, was a magnet for young, hard-working immigrants.

Once again drawing upon GE News articles from the period, I discovered that both grandfathers were working at the Schenectady GE plant in 1925, although there is no evidence the two knew each other. The articles do indicate that Antonio worked as a switchboard assembler in Building 23, but I don't have any indication of just how long he worked at the Schenectady plant. If he was still employed at GE in 1929, he must have taken a leave to travel back to Italy, since he married my Grandmother Maddalena (aka Lena) there later that year. Apparently, the two had been acquainted through other relatives in what was most likely an "arranged" marriage common in those times.

It is not clear if my Grandfather Antonio went back to GE in late 1929 or 1930 for a time, or if he had already gained enough electrical expertise to obtain his independent electrical contractors license. In any event, at about this time, he did acquire his electrical contractor license. Armed with this ticket to his next stop in the American Dream, he was self-employed at this trade for the remainder of his working life. Many of the homes in our old Mont Pleasant neighborhood, including the house I grew up in, bear witness to his work. Like so many others, he used his strong work ethic, self-taught skills, fast-learning ability, and perseverance to overcome his limited English language skills and formal educational deficiencies.

With a stable employment situation, Antonio and Lena started their own family. Their first daughter, Carmelinda, better known as Melinda, was born in September 1930. She would become my mother. Two other children, Gertrude (1933) and Nicholas (1934) followed, and now the Iacobucci side of my immigrant family was well established.

WWII was a catalyst that independently drew both of my grandmothers to GE. The male-dominated workforce was greatly depleted by the war, and women stepped in to fill the gap[3]. Driven by economic need and presented

---

3 Refer to the book titled "Electric City" by Julia Kirk Blackwelder for some fascinating portraits of GE management and ethos, particularly with respect toward women in the work force.

with opportunity, both grandmothers joined the GE workforce during the mid1940s. A GE Works News photo and caption from 1955 indicates that both grandmothers were still employed there in the mid-1950s. Just prior to publishing this book I discovered my grandmother Maddalena's Certificate of Service acknowledging her 14 years and 5 months of service as she retired on Oct. 1, 1958.

In researching this book, I made a very startling and moving discovery from two short GE News notes published in 1944. Following a family visit to Italy in the late 1930s, my Iacobucci grandparents decided to leave their young son, Nicholas, then only about 4 years old, with family when they returned to the US. Unfortunately, WWII broke out much sooner in Europe, which effectively trapped young Nicholas, a US citizen by birth, in a war zone for the duration of WWII. While employed at GE in 1944 and desperate to learn about her only son and other relatives, my Grandmother Maddalena placed the following request in the January 21, 1944 GE News:

> *Mrs. A. IACOBUCCI, of the Turbine stockroom, is anxious to hear from her son, NICOLA IACOBUCCI, 9 years old, an American citizen, living with his grandmother, Mrs. Vincenza Musco in Caiazzo, Provincia of Benevento, Italy or with her brother, Pasquale Musco in Castel Campagnano, Provincia of Benevento. Any one knowing of his whereabouts, please communicate with her at [address], Schenectady, N. Y.*

Grandma inserted this ad because she knew that copies of the GE News were being distributed to US troops overseas who were employed at GE in Schenectady before the war. In what must be the most miraculous of outcomes, the following response appeared in the March 24, 1944 GE News:

> *Mrs. LENA IACOBUCCI wishes to extend many thanks, through this column, to Pfc. J. VISCUSI, a native of Schenectady, who is serving with the armed forces overseas. 'Pfc. Viscusi read in the GE WORKS NEWS that Mrs. Iacobucci would like to obtain news of relatives in the war district, and he was able to visit those relatives and relay the good news to her that they are safe and well.*

This is a stunning story, and it shows the amazing goodness in people in general and GE folks in particular. While my grandmother's plea and the ensuing response is a poignant example, readers will discover the theme of strong bonds among GE co-workers, repeated throughout this book. I hope someday I can locate the relatives of PFC Viscusi and thank them again, but for now I'll extend a special note of gratitude and appreciation here.

So, the foundation of my American dream was laid by my four grandparents, who were drawn to the GE Company by similar circumstances. I felt it was important to begin my book with this prologue to briefly document their pertinent immigrant experience and also because each of them preceded me at GE. What is fascinating to me about my grandparents is that with so little formal education, a limited ability to communicate in English, and very sharp cultural differences, they somehow managed to be hired and perform useful work in one of America's most prominent companies. It certainly is a testament to their struggles, determination and willingness to sacrifice as they worked toward their dreams.

They passed these traits on to each of their children, and through my parents, these same characteristics were passed to my sister Elaine, to me and to others of our generation. All of this makes me feel blessed and privileged for being afforded educational opportunities that neither my grandparents nor my parents had. Without question, the success I enjoyed during my 40-year professional GE career was directly related to the sacrifices my grandparents and parents made, and the outstanding educational opportunities my sister and I experienced were critical in each of our own professions.

Education remains the foundation upon which everyone can still realize their own American dream. If you take nothing away from reading this book, then know that the most important thing you can do for yourself is to obtain a solid education and never quit working toward your dream.

Chapter 1

A FOOT IN THE DOOR

WE ALL HAVE TO START SOMEWHERE, and the pivotal moment for me came on May 5, 1961. On that date, the good sisters at Our Lady of Mt. Carmel elementary school allowed us to watch the live television broadcast of Alan Sheppard's sub-orbital Mercury launch, an historic first for the US-manned space program. Watching that broadcast lit a life-long passion in me for all things science, space and technology.

During the 1960s, I was transfixed by everything related to space flight. Just as all good sports fans know the players and stats from their favorite teams, I memorized astronaut and spacecraft names along with assorted facts about each. I can unequivocally state that I watched every Mercury, Gemini and Apollo launch live, even if it meant being "sick" from school just to make sure I could get to a TV.

Captivated by every space adventure, I spent long hours listening to my favorite newscaster, Walter Cronkite, eloquently explaining the details of each mission. Even when problems arose and launches were delayed by long countdown "holds," sometimes resulting in postponements, there was always the fascinating coverage commentary. Cronkite would professionally fill the airtime with seemingly endless scientific information on the astronauts, their training, and mission details, which I absorbed like water on a dry sponge.

I identified with my space heroes and emulated them in my play and projects. Mock "spacecraft" were constructed in my yard as I re-enacted countless launches and embarked on imaginary missions. I often enlisted my younger cousin Karen as my test astronaut while I ran "mission control." She still reminds me to this day of the time I left her talking into our "intercom system" as I took a break for lunch, but forgot to notify her.

Years later, in 1967, I vividly recall the tragic news of the Apollo 1 fire, which took the lives of astronauts Gus Grissom, Ed White and Roger Chaffee. This fatal launch pad event hit me with overwhelming emotional impact, as if I had personally lost close friends. Up until that accident, my astronaut heroes seemed invincible. The Apollo 1 accident was a stunning wake-up call, both to me and the nation, which dramatically underscored the very real dangers associated with manned space flight.

Nearly a decade of live space launch coverage culminated with the first moon landing in July 1969. As with most epic events, I remember exactly where I was during the historic Apollo 11 moon landing—glued to a television at my Aunt Gina's (mom's younger sister) home watching with her and my cousin Karen (my stand-in play astronaut). It was appropriate that I was at Aunt Gina's home, as both she and her husband, Uncle Henry Frick, motivated me in those formative years by sharing stories of their own interesting work experiences.

My Aunt Gina worked at GE in the mid-1950s as an executive secretary. In her position, she was directly exposed to many GE technical professionals, so she could share first-hand knowledge from her own experiences. Uncle Henry had trained in what was then the GE Apprentice program before pursuing other opportunities, so he had good mechanical and other technical expertise to pass along as well.

In the late 1950s, my aunt took a major career risk and left her executive assistant role at GE, along with a number of her associates. With GE's permission, they formed a consulting business called Value Analysis, Inc. The venture turned out to be very successful for both my aunt and later, Uncle Henry, who ultimately joined her at Value Analysis. They both became key players in this tiny company that grew to have an impressive global consulting footprint with offices on four continents. My mom also found some part-time employment at Value Analysis during busy periods. Even my younger sister Elaine, Cousin Karen and I sometimes helped out with collating and other small office tasks during summers and school breaks.

My aunt and uncle were good role models who encouraged us to study for college and prepare for work as professionals. Certainly, it was a privilege to receive this informal, yet timely, business exposure in a very small company setting with such a global footprint. For me especially, the experience provided an initial awareness of global connections that emanated from tiny Schenectady, New York.

I remember always being fascinated by giant world maps that hung in offices at Value Analysis' Schenectady branch. The maps contained small colored pins, some marking other branch locations, while others depicted sites for upcoming seminars. I spent hours studying these maps, wondering what it would be like to visit these intriguing distant places. My fascination with maps drove me to mount a world map in my bedroom. To this day, there is both a map and a giant glass globe in my home office. Little did I realize that, in the future, I would have the opportunity to visit many intriguing places that had captivated my imagination as a youngster.

Of course, education was the critical enabler for me. A solid education was the great equalizer that literally unlocked a world of opportunity. Not only was I fortunate to attend excellent private parochial elementary and middle school, but I later also attended an outstanding local public high school, Mont Pleasant, then renowned for its college preparatory and technical programs. The technical curriculum was so good at Mont Pleasant that other area schools bussed in their top students to take classes there during the 1970s. My strong internal technical passion, combined with an aptitude for science and math, made study in these subject areas relatively easily for me. My high school grades landed me in the academic top 10% and earned National Honor Society recognition, which opened the door to a wide selection of colleges.

My first choice was to attend local, historic Union College in Schenectady. Unfortunately, I was not accepted at Union, primarily due to Union's self-imposed quota on local acceptances. My other two college choices, Syracuse University and the University of South Florida in Tampa, both did extend acceptances to me. After visiting both schools, I opted for South Florida, which boasted highly rated educational offerings in multiple science and engineering disciplines. To be honest, the warm, sunny Florida climate also swayed my thinking, as it seemed much more appealing than the cold, gray, snowy Syracuse winters. The Tampa area also was already familiar to me; my grandfather Antonio had built a home in nearby St. Petersburg in the 1950s, and the family regularly vacationed there as I was growing up.

But, surprisingly, after two years at South Florida studying engineering and other arts and sciences electives, I found myself tiring of the monotonous Florida climate and missing the seasonal changes of the northeast. At the end of my sophomore year, in 1974, South Florida awarded me an Associate of Arts and Sciences diploma, signifying that I had successfully completed the requisite number of courses in five required disciplines. If ever there was a time to consider a change, this was it.

After a transfer admission rejection from Union College, I somewhat hesitantly applied to Rensselaer Polytechnic Institute (RPI), located near my hometown in Troy, New York. While RPI was an extremely prominent undergraduate engineering college, with worldwide recognition, I had never pictured myself going there, subjectively considering it much too "nerdy." However, my opinion was swayed after visiting the campus and meeting with the engineering dean.

RPI accepted me as a junior transfer, fully recognizing my Associate degree from South Florida. I was even offered a substantial academic scholarship to bolster my dwindling finances. So, in the summer of 1974, literally halfway through college, I made the pivotal decision to return home to attend RPI, locking in on its aero-mechanical engineering degree program.

With my college plans now solidified, I needed to find a summer job. One of my best leads came from my Aunt Gina, who had moved on from Value Analysis and was then the career placement director at nearby Schenectady County Community College (SCCC). In her role, Aunt Gina maintained close contacts with area employers as she strived to find both internships and permanent positions for SCCC students. After successfully placing several of her students at GE, she recognized that GE still had unfulfilled needs, so she encouraged me to apply to GE as well.

Being very naïve, I confidently walked into the GE employment building on the sprawling Schenectady campus, only to be abruptly told there would be no hiring at GE that summer. Devastated by this news, I marched directly over to my aunt's office at SCCC and explained what had happened. Over a quick ego-rebuilding lunch, my aunt suggested I try a different approach and go speak directly with the manager[4] of Schenectady Instrumentation Services (SIS), then part of GE's Apparatus Services Business Division, located in Building 28. From prior conversations, my aunt knew that SIS had a huge backlog of work and was actively trying to find qualified help. Following my aunt's advice, I called SIS and, to my amazement, I was invited to come over that very afternoon for an interview.

---

4 Early lesson – Always go to the top and make sure you speak with the person who can make things happen.

Armed with renewed hope and my latest resume, I headed back to the GE campus for the second time. Bypassing the employment office, I walked confidently right through the employee entrance nearest to Building 28. Luckily, the gate guards made no attempt to stop or question me.

At GE there was no nearby parking for Building 28, so I probably walked about a half mile from the nearest visitor parking lot to the building itself. It was an unusually hot, humid June day, but in the bright sunshine, I was in an upbeat mood. Upon arriving in the lobby, I noticed a plaque indicating the managers' office was located on the fifth (top) floor of the building. The only problem was that the one obvious elevator was not in service, so I headed for the adjacent stairway.

Here I was in for a major challenge. Building 28, built in the WWII era, was a well-constructed, concrete reinforced structure, with double high floors. I had to climb 10 flights of stairs, two for each floor, with perhaps 30 steps per flight, each flight separated by a landing to allow for the 180-degree turns toward the next set of steps.

Even though I was only 20 and in decent physical shape, the challenging climb left me winded. By the time I reached the top, perspiration was evident on my face, and I was breathing heavily. But, instead of taking a moment to compose myself, I headed straight for the air-conditioned office area, quickly opening the door and bursting inside. To my surprise, the executive secretary was seated immediately inside the entrance. She was startled by my entrance. I must have been a comical sight as I struggled to catch my breath and speak, but she apparently surmised that I had just hiked the stairs. As I introduced myself, she directed me to a chair and explained that there was a "back" service elevator I could have used. Good lesson for any future visits!

Just as I reached a visitor chair to begin composing myself, the SIS manager himself stepped out to investigate the commotion caused by my arrival. Still with barely time to catch my breath, I stood and shook his hand while again introducing myself. He smiled and invited me into his office for a brief interview. Apparently, I passed his initial screening, so after a short period, the SIS manager signaled for one of his subordinates.

As it turned out, the subordinate was a big imposing man named Bob, who was the actual hiring manager. Bob's physical appearance reminded me of Ed Asner, who played Lou Grant on the old Mary Tyler Moore TV show.

With long sleeves rolled back and tie loosened about his broad neck, the resemblance to Asner's character was uncanny. And, as I would discover, in keeping with the Lou Grant personality, Bob's burly and stern exterior concealed a very fair and kind person underneath.

Bob conducted a thorough interview, covering my experience, electrical work skills, plans of study, and a host of other questions. Both he and his boss seemed impressed that I was headed to RPI to study engineering, as RPI graduates had very solid reputations within GE. My decision to transfer to RPI was already paying an unexpected early dividend, even before I attended a single class!

Apparently, my interview went quite well because Bob offered me a summer position on the spot! As we got into specifics, he explained, somewhat apologetically that my starting pay would be $4 per hour, which was under the stated normal rate for the position. He went on to explain that my compensation would be periodically raised in steps up to the standard $5.50 per hour rate, based on performance. When asked if this was acceptable, I could barely contain my elation as I shook hands to acknowledge my approval. What Bob did not know was that his offer was the best I had ever had for any summer job. Previously, the most I had ever earned was something like $2.50 per hour on hard labor jobs. In any case, not only was the salary terrific, but I would have a chance to work at the iconic General Electric Company, then the most prominent and prestigious employer in my hometown.

So just like that, I had landed my first GE job! On my very first day at GE, I discovered that my old Mont Pleasant classmate, Lou Mazzone, had also recently starting working at SIS. Lou had just completed two years of pre-engineering study at SCCC, and my Aunt Gina had also helped him find the position at GE. What a pleasant coincidence to have a familiar face working nearby.

That entire summer working at GE was just incredible. I was assigned to perform various tasks involving calibration and repair of all types of analog measurement devices that were widely used in the mid-1970s. These included voltmeters, ammeters, multi-meters, shunt resistors and similar devices. SIS offered unique calibration traceability back to the National Bureau of Standards, and I was properly instructed in these practices.

Working at SIS afforded me exposure to the Measurement Services Engineering team, a sub-group within SIS that specialized in complex technical measurements. The Measurement Services group took on unique and challenging measurements of all kinds, often using the latest available new digital devices. The group even had thermographic specialists with infrared cameras that inspected power lines, transformers and other equipment. Working with the Measurement Services guys was really an unexpected bonus that later would pay much bigger dividends than I ever imagined.

While I was absorbing every experience thoroughly each day and totally enjoying my job, others were observing me. In the 1970s, contractual services was a new, lucrative and growing business area for GE. SIS fell under what was then known as the Apparatus Services Business Division (ASBD) of GE. ASBD's new business model expanded on the concept of specialized equipment rental to incorporate engineering expertise to perform measurements, analyze data and recommend remedial solutions. Fate had once again landed me in a situation where my work had caught the eye of the growing Measurement Services group. This lucky break would have a huge impact on my future with GE.

Within a few weeks, I was given the first of multiple incremental hourly pay raises. Several weeks later another raise followed, so that prior to leaving in September to attend college, I had achieved the full-position rate of pay. When it came time for me to leave to attend classes at RPI, Bob and the team at SIS asked me to consider a follow-on work assignment during our December/January break. I thanked them, and told them I definitely would be in touch about returning.

In fact, I did return to work for just over two months in December 1974 and into February 1975 before again returning to full-time college studies. In the mid-1970s, RPI had an unusual "J-Term" between fall and spring semesters. Students were offered flexible studies in special one-month courses or worked on specially approved projects. My GE assignment counted as a special project, so I continued working well into February 1975. Upon completing that stint, once again the SIS team asked me to consider returning for a third assignment for the summer of 1975, and I agreed to do so.

During the late spring of 1975, SIS once again had a backlog of work and attempted to rehire me. In fact, they considered having me work with the Measurement Services Engineering group for part of the assignment, which would have been great. But, for reasons I can't completely recall, possibly related to local union and overtime pay issues, all summer 1975 hiring within GE's Schenectady plant was suspended. What a huge disappointment! But like so many other disappointments I was to experience, there was a silver lining, as chance and circumstances worked silently to influence my destiny. Meanwhile, I'll always be grateful to Bob for taking a chance by hiring an unproven 20-year-old during that summer of 1974.

In the summer of 1975, I ended up working an outdoor labor job with the Schenectady City School District. My dad had helped arrange for me to return to the job, which I had previously worked in 1973. Dad told me hard labor work would help build character, but it only seemed to foster frustration, and the hot, humid summer weather did little to console me. Anyway, I gritted my teeth and worked through it. Yet, as it turned out, my misfortune became a catalyst that enabled positive consequences that played out over the next year.

Because I needed a diversion from the monotonous labor job and also wished to ease my senior year class workload, I decided to take a required engineering economics course in the evenings at nearby Union College. Yes, this is the same Union College that had twice rejected my formal undergraduate applications.

As it turned out, I did extremely well in this class, but more importantly I met and formed a solid connection with my instructor, Dr. Ram Mittal. In a few short weeks, as I got to know Dr. Mittal much better, I discovered we shared common interests in both energy and transportation. Following one of our discussions, Professor Mittal invited me to attend an energy and transportation seminar he was hosting later that summer. The deal was that I could attend the seminar free of charge, in exchange for my assistance with logistics—a fair trade in my book.

The week-long seminar turned out to be an eye opener for me on several levels. Certainly, I gained valuable perspectives on current policies and issues facing the US in the post-oil embargo world. I also made some beneficial professional contacts with companies like Boeing, while gaining an appreciation for the effort required to organize and execute professional technical conferences. All of this would prove valuable later in my own professional career.

Following the seminar, Professor Mittal and I met to discuss future plans. I learned that he would be teaching his specialty Transportation Engineering course that fall, and he invited me to consider taking it. He further explained that Union College and RPI participated in a little-known reciprocal educational consortium. Under this agreement, students in one institution could take classes at a "partner" school if a particular course was not offered at their primary school. Since this was the case, I ended up taking the fall Transportation Engineering course at Union College.

Dr. Mittal's course filled in many topics that had been discussed at the seminar and broadened my overall knowledge of energy efficiency as related to automobiles, trains and aircraft, among other modes. I especially enjoyed the sessions dealing with aircraft engines.

Partway through the course, Dr. Mittal asked me to consider a senior project in my final senior spring semester. Again, such a project—if approved—could be covered under the same consortium agreement. Essentially, the project would build upon knowledge gained in both the summer seminar and the current transportation course. In fact, I also was able to leverage some of my seminar contacts, with Boeing and other companies, who supplied me with crucial information. I'm most grateful for meeting, knowing and learning from Dr. Mittal, who was such a positive influence on me at a critical time in my young life.

In hindsight, it is evident to me that fate had once again intervened in my life. The lost opportunity of employment at GE in the summer of 1975 led me down a road I likely would not have taken—with very beneficial consequences. In yet another curious twist, despite two undergraduate rejections for admission, I ended up taking three senior-level courses (counting my senior project) at Union, earning A's in all of them! Funny how things work out.

As I worked my way through the spring semester, my focus again shifted to employment opportunities, which were sparse in the spring of 1976. Again, I contacted the SIS team to inquire about full-time positions. Since their business was continuing to grow, I was advised that GE planned to make me a formal employment offer based on performance on my prior assignments. I couldn't have been more thrilled.

However, just to complicate matters a bit, as I approached my RPI graduation, Professor Mittal offered me a fellowship opportunity to continue graduate studies with him at Union College. Now, I had two viable options for the next chapter of my life.

Ultimately, I chose to accept the GE offer as a Measurement Services engineer for several good reasons, not the least of which was, for me, a staggering student loan debt of nearly $10,000. Really, more importantly, I had always considered employment at GE a very special opportunity. So, despite the tempting offer to continue my association with Dr. Mittal, I chose to work in a professional capacity for the iconic hometown company that had once employed my grandparents.

At my RPI commencement ceremony, yet another one of those unusual coincidences occurred that seemed to signal that I was correctly following my internal career compass. As unbelievable as it may seem, the person selected to deliver the keynote address for RPI's bi-centennial class of 1976 was none other than Walter Cronkite, one of the most popular and trusted news broadcasters of all time. To this day I am still astounded by the fact that this most famous newsman, whom I had listened to for so many hours through all those Project Mercury, Gemini and Apollo launches during the 1960s, was chosen to deliver such a memorable and inspiring talk at my undergraduate commencement. How fitting that the man who helped cultivate my interest in science and engineering gave the keynote address as I received my Bachelor of Engineering degree!

And thus my GE career was poised to begin. The Measurement Services group at GE asked me to report for my first day of professional work on Monday, May 17, 1976, a mere three days after my RPI commencement exercises. Little did I realize what I was in for. My first year at GE was to be one of the most unusual, and yet tumultuous, of my entire career.

Chapter 2

THIS JOB IS FOR THE BIRDS

I'm amazed that I was neither fired nor killed in my first year at GE. That's no exaggeration, for two reasons. First, I ended up reporting to a new person, who turned out to be one of the most ruthless and unscrupulous individuals I would ever encounter at GE. Second, my formal safety training was virtually non-existent, thereby increasing my risk exposure as I was sent to the field. Somehow—as you'll see in later chapters—chance, good luck or whatever controls our destiny, was on my side, and the ultimate outcomes of my experiences turned out surprisingly well, but the ride was extremely wild, and the dangers quite real.

Approximately six months before I began my professional GE career, a seemingly completely unrelated event took place that would impact me on my very first day of work. In November 1975, a DC-10 cargo aircraft crashed on takeoff at New York's JFK airport. Luckily, no one was killed in this accident, which later was attributed to bird ingestion in one or more of the DC-10's three giant CF-6 engines, which were manufactured by GE. Ramifications from this accident, and other similar events involving GE's CF-6 equipped aircraft, triggered events leading to my first GE professional assignment.

On the first Monday I reported to GE, I was euphoric. A fantastic opportunity was before me, and I was determined to be successful. Following in the footsteps of my grandparents, who had struggled in blue collar assignments, here I was, the first person in my family to become a professional employee with the iconic American company. The company, known by two capital letters, was not only recognized in every US household, but virtually everywhere in the modern world. There was no way I could imagine the incredible experiences, wide-ranging travel opportunities, wonderful people nor the magnitude of challenges that would come my way. At almost every step I would be privileged to work with some of the best professionals in the entire company.

Quickly that first morning, I learned of many organizational changes on the Measurement Services team since my earlier assignments. A number of new engineers were now on staff, along with several core members I had previously met. Also, a new manager had been assigned to the Measurement Services engineers. I will refer to him only by his initials, DK, for reasons that will become apparent. I knew absolutely nothing about DK. Certainly, he wasn't the fellow I had planned to work with. He had not interviewed me, nor had he written my offer letter, and he definitely didn't have any first-hand knowledge of my prior work experience at SIS.

This scenario—of hiring managers changing soon after I accepted a new role—would be repeated multiple times throughout my career. Each time, it was uncomfortable and disruptive. I often had difficulty adjusting to these situations, particularly when I had established a strong rapport with the hiring manager, only to have some type of upheaval in the first weeks or months of a new role disrupt things. In this particular case, I didn't even report to the hiring manager for a single day! There would be absolutely no "adjustment" time here as I was immediately launched on my first unique assignment.

While sitting at my desk and trying to familiarize myself with a myriad of orientation material, forms, and procedures, I was interrupted in the first hours by a supervising engineer. He inquired if I could travel the next morning to New Jersey with another GE employee from GE Global Research on what would become a most unusual multi-month assignment. When I answered in the affirmative, he told me to drop everything and accompany him as I was about to get a crash course on my new assignment. So, before I could even complete any of the benefit forms or sign-in paperwork, without any formal orientation whatsoever, I was taken to a meeting in another building.

As I quickly learned, the project would involve a field acoustic experiment to investigate the impact of jet engine noise, particularly GE's newly launched high bypass ratio[5] CF6 engine, on seagulls. The chosen location was Brigantine National Wildlife Refuge located in Oceanville, New Jersey, about a 30 minute drive north of Atlantic City, New Jersey. The refuge had granted permission for us to conduct our experiments there. Like many assignments that would

---

5 High bypass ratio simply means that much of the air entering the large front engine fan actually bypasses the core compressor, combustor and turbine. Most of the engine thrust is created by this fan, which in turn is driven by the core turbine. Prior engines developed most or all of their thrust directly from the core turbine.

follow, this project proved to be extremely interesting and most unusual. Also, like many others that followed, this project would immediately catapult me into work with some of the top experts in the company.

Only in hindsight did I recognize that fate—from the crash of that DC-10 months prior to my start date—once again had intervened in my career, even before it officially started. Somehow my desire to work on gas turbines, particularly aircraft engines, was magically handed to me on my very first professional assignment. How fortunate was that? You just can't script things any better!

As I later learned, the JFK DC-10 incident was one of several caused by bird strikes involving GE's newly introduced CF-6 engine. At the time a theory was circulating that perhaps the new engine had sound emanations that somehow attracted the birds. With GE's reputation at stake, combined with heavy competition from the likes of Pratt & Whitney and Rolls Royce, GE decided to embark on an unusual program to investigate, and hopefully disprove, this theory.

Drawing on some of the top relevant technical experts in the company, a GE team was quickly pulled together. The team included two leading GE acoustic experts, a PhD named Richard from our world-class GE Global Research and a sharp German fellow named Horst Hehmann, who was GE Aircraft Engines' top noise expert. A leading ornithologist, Dr. Michael S, from a leading East Coast university, would provide avian expertise.

Although completely unknown to me at the time, the group also previously had consulted with one of GE's top statisticians, Dr. Gerald Hahn[6], for advice on how to construct a statistically meaningful series of tests[7] for the given objective. As the team came together, everyone recognized that specialized equipment was needed and, of course, someone to operate this equipment. Enter the Measurement Services group, and one newly hired engineer. Lo and behold, just a couple of hours into my professional career, I was now being called to duty on a very elite team.

After a fairly short initial meeting, I discovered that I had less than 24 hours to assemble equipment, learn how to use it, and then embark on a

---

6 Years later I would again encounter Hahn as an adjunct professor teaching a segment of my graduate program statistics class at Union College.

7 Later in GE's Six Sigma period, this type of testing was known in statistical nomenclature as Design of Experiments. Hahn later published a paper titled "Practical Considerations in Designing Experiments" by GJ Hahn, Report 82CRD228, September 1982.

multi-day trip. During this time, I had a most extraordinary and memorable experience in an anechoic chamber[8] within the Schenectady plant. Briefly, the room was a giant cube, perhaps 10 to 12 feet on a side with only a single, heavy freezer-like acoustic door. Every internal surface inside the chamber was lined with cone-like foam material. When entering the room, I "walked" on suspended steel wire cables arranged to form a mesh with about 2-inch squares. As I stepped inside this chamber, the steel cables had some flex, like walking on a trampoline, and the open mesh created the illusion I was walking on air. Inside was the quietest environment I had ever experienced. Calibrating our sound equipment in this chamber was very surreal.

As plans crystalized, I learned that testing would involve playing a series of jet engine takeoff sounds around a large pond within the wildlife preserve where many wild seagulls would gather. As a control to our experiment, we randomized the jet engine model acoustic sequence and mixed in other "control" type bird calls.

My Measurement Services group supplied the latest battery-powered Nagra reel-to-reel tape player/recorders for this project. Given that I would be operating in the field, an inverter to generate AC power from DC was also required, as the amplifier/speaker system required AC power to broadcast sounds at required decibel levels. Field power was supplied by 12-volt motorcycle batteries, which I recharged when necessary.

On my second day, I loaded the equipment into a car, and along with my new acoustic GE research associate, drove to Atlantic City to meet Dr. Michael and Horst Hehmann. During the trip, I had time to reflect on how interesting this first assignment was going to be. I was going to be working with aircraft engines (or at least noises from aircraft engines) in a fun setting on the south Jersey shore in early summer. What a cool and unusual start to my career!

When we arrived in Atlantic City, the vintage seaside resort was showing its age and reflecting years of neglect. It would be two more years before the first casino arrived to inject new hope into the place. Meanwhile, Dr. Richard and I met the others on the team. Horst Hehmann was a solid, smart GE technical expert. He was also a very personable guy, and we became quick friends as we both shared a common love of aviation. Our ornithologist Dr. Michael

---

8 An anechoic chamber is a non-reflecting or echo-free room designed to almost completely absorb sound waves. Such a room is also completely isolated from external noise sources.

S. was a casual, pipe-smoking academician, who openly shared his ideas with us. I considered myself most fortunate to be working with such a terrific team of experts. These folks were the first of what was to be an incredibly long list of talented and interesting people I would encounter throughout my career.

Not long into our initial meeting, we determined that the jet engine tapes we planned to use were of inferior quality for our needs. I suggested that perhaps we could travel to Philadelphia International Airport, only an hour away, to record new tapes. All the aircraft we were interested in regularly operated out of PHL (the airport code for Philadelphia). Although the team was somewhat reluctant to accept my suggestion, Hehmann immediately nominated me to contact PHL and make an inquiry. Wisely, the team advised me to identify ourselves as being associated with a university study. Technically, our university professor, Dr. Michael S, fulfilled that description, so that was what I did. The thinking here was that PHL would be more receptive toward helping a university study rather than a corporate endeavor.

So, I made the call to Philadelphia International airport and convinced the security folks there to allow us to make the measurements. We were told to arrive at the airport the next morning, and contact security upon arrival. I can't imagine being given the same privileges in today's world of tightened airport security.

The next day, we all piled into a single car, with equipment loaded in the trunk and headed to PHL. Security, consisting simply of a pickup truck equipped with flashing yellow strobes and two team members escorted us to a grassy area adjacent to the active runway, near the "rotation" point of departing aircraft. Here, we set up to record various aircraft takeoff sound levels.

I became an instant hero on the team for my efforts. And, Hehmann and the team also were impressed that I could identify every one of the various commercial aircraft operating as well as the specific engines on those aircraft. A good portion of my knowledge came from the prior summer, where I had made connections with a Boeing representative at Professor Mittal's energy seminar. Hours of working with the Boeing aircraft and engine manufacturer brochures paid nice dividends. It is just fantastic how seemingly unrelated events all tie together!

Over about two hours or so we obtained excellent data and headed back to New Jersey to edit our new tapes. I can only wonder how many complaints were registered at that hotel that night as we edited the tapes and played them at actual sound levels. Pictures on the wall nearly vibrated off their hooks. In any case, we obtained realistic tapes, so now it was off to the wildlife preserve.

Brigantine National Wildlife preserve had a fairly robust population of laughing, herring and, most importantly, the infamous great black back gulls. The latter gulls were associated with the DC10 incident at JFK airport. Yes, during the summer of 1976, working alongside our expert ornithologist, Dr. Michael S., I learned more about seagulls than I ever imagined.

For the next several weeks, I regularly commuted to work via air, flying from Albany airport (ALB) to Atlantic City through Philadelphia (PHL). From PHL, I took a small commuter flight directly to tiny Bader Field, which was less than a mile from the beach in downtown Atlantic City (AC).

Dr. Michael and I planned each day at the preserve with a randomized sequence of tape sounds. We also varied our broadcast locations. Depending on location, I sometimes operated out of a small pup tent to shade me from the hot sun and give me some relief from the constant annoyance of biting green-headed flies. My job was to operate the tape players, amplifier, speakers and other equipment. I also assisted the professor with bird activity observations after each broadcast. Everything was dutifully recorded in a detailed test log.

As I recall, we had a sequence of about seven or eight tapes, including sounds of GE's CF-6, as well as competitor engine takeoff sounds. Each individual sequence was played once each hour. During the broadcast of engine takeoffs, the sound was repeatedly played about four times, with each successive play increasing sound levels so we could have some idea of levels that impacted the birds. A couple of "control" tapes actually contained wild bird distress calls, and these always caused the most startling reactions from wild gulls. Whenever we played the very realistic-sounding distress calls, the birds quickly scattered, with some circling high above my speaker to investigate. That reaction provided a level of confirmation that we were broadcasting authentic sound quality. What a way to start my career with GE, chasing seagulls in a wildlife preserve in the heat of summer at a south Jersey resort location[9].

The data was collected and analyzed, and various reports were written. I still have a copy of Dr. Michael's draft summary paper, but GE was very guard-

---

9 Dr. Michael S. and I operated out of a beach front motel on Brigantine Island, just north of Atlantic City.

ed about what, if any, material was ever used in meetings with the FAA. I have to believe that there was sufficient evidence to convince anyone that the CF-6 engine did not "attract" gulls[10]. One subsequent finding in the JFK crash investigation was that there was a large trash landfill not far from the runways. The landfill provided an attractive food source that was considered a prime contributor to attracting gulls. I believe the landfill was eventually closed, perhaps partially due to results from the investigation.

Bird and aircraft collisions continue to challenge aviation today. Most folks recall the "Miracle on the Hudson" incident with a US Air jet operating out of LaGuardia airport a few years back. Larger, quieter engines capable of accelerating planes quite rapidly are a challenge to slower flying birds. Constant vigilance is always required, but future collisions do still seem inevitable.

My first professional work experience was a really good one, and I gained tremendous insights working together in a team environment as we solved unusual, challenging problems. I'm very grateful to each of these men for contributing to my overall learning experience.

And learn I did, exposed as I was to many new topics that went well beyond just providing "measurement services." I certainly didn't have an awareness or appreciation back then for the constant learning that would be part of every project and person I met.

It was also quite rewarding for me to be able to contribute in my own way to the project. In addition to solving almost daily equipment issues, my suggestion and follow-on execution to obtain higher quality acoustic recordings at Philadelphia greatly benefited the project. Leveraging my commercial aircraft and engine knowledge was a bonus. It also served as a reminder that you never know when seemingly insignificant learning opportunities pay dividends.

What an interesting, fun and most unusual start to my GE career. Yet even more stimulating, one-of-a-kind assignments were headed my way.

---

10 I doubt anyone really believed that any aircraft engine actually attracts birds. One observation I regularly heard after completing this project was that the newer engines were much quieter, so during takeoff they would get closer to nearby birds before the sound level was perceived to be a threat. By that point the aircraft is moving faster and this, combined with a much larger front fan area (>8 ft. diameter), decreases a bird's ability to escape.

Chapter 3

NEXT UP

By late July 1976 I finally again began regularly reporting to the office. Boy did that feel strange after nearly two full months on the road. Naturally there was quite a bit to catch up on. First I had to complete my "new hire" forms from my first week which were still incomplete. Human Resources (HR) was certainly not pleased that I had not finished much of the required paperwork, although I had only been following my manager's directions. Certainly my manager must be happy that I was generating so much billable time for the group. But even here I encountered some issues.

I quickly discovered there was this thing called "Expense Reports", more commonly known as an Expense Accounts. No one had instructed me on how to complete these in the "GE system", and because of this I was many weeks in arrears. My air tickets, which had been provided each week by our travel agency, were being charged to my expense report. Unfortunately, weeks had elapsed with no employee reconciliation. Now my new boss was displeased that I hadn't completed any reports at all. It seems no one instructed me about this practice, nor was I intuitive enough to ask. Complicating the situation was the fact that I had discarded all my air ticket receipts. Not a great start for the new guy.

Luckily the airlines agreed to send me duplicate copy of my ticket charges which remedied that issue. As it turned out, GE owed me, or more precisely my dad, quite a sum of money since I had been charging many expenses using my dad's MasterCard[11]. If anyone should have been upset by the expense report logistics delay it should have been my dad. During the next week or so, I caught up on all delinquent expense reports as my next assignments loomed.

My ability to land unusual assignments did not end with the initial seagull job. Yet another extraordinary project immediately emerged in the summer of 1976. Again it involved the CF-6 engine, but this time not on an aircraft. With a number of modifications, GE had adapted this very success-

---

11   After college graduation, heavily in debt with no job history I didn't qualify for my own credit card.

ful aircraft engine to a marine version, by removing the large fan at the front of the engine. Additionally, other changes, including a re-packaged engine enclosure, adapted this turbine for use as primary propulsion on ships. The highly efficient and relatively compact size made this engine ideal for ship propulsion. GE was quick to recognize the opportunity and built variants of the CF6, known as the LM2500[12], for marine use.

But typical of many new product applications, the LM2500 initially had issues when first adapted to a marine setting. Not surprisingly, the compressor and turbine blading were impacted by the corrosive, moist, salt-laden sea environment. Remember these engines originally were designed to operate in the relatively dry, thin air at 35,000 feet so operating them in an ocean environment presented new challenges. Complicating the situation, many marine engines were being operated with less expensive, lower grade fuels in ship board applications which introduced further problems. Still, usage of the compact, powerful and efficient LM2500 had caught the eyes of the US Navy which, at the time, was considering these gas turbines to power the next new class of destroyers[13] and possibly other vessels. But first GE would have to address the ocean environmental challenges.

Once again the GE Aviation team, based in Cincinnati, Ohio contacted our Schenectady, New York based Measurement Services team and requested our assistance. Plans called for shipboard testing of an LM2500 powered Merchant Marine vessel named the GTS Admiral Callaghan[14]. At the time the Callaghan was contracted by the US Military Sea Lift Command (MSC) and was operating on regular runs between Bayonne, New Jersey and Bremerhaven, Germany. The US Navy had chosen this ship as a study vessel to better evaluate the LM2500 engines for potential use in naval ship propulsion.

In addition to engine performance parameters, the planned measurement study would attempt to gain more detailed information on actual sodium levels reaching the engine inlet downstream of the filter/demisters. Given my great love of gas turbine engines, I accepted the offer to support

---

12 LM stood for Land Marine and was a GE designation for both land based and water applications for the popular core of its CF6 aircraft engine, sometimes called a derivative engine.

13 US Navy DD963 Spruance Class Destroyers were the new class at this time.

14 Named after US Navy Admiral William M. Callaghan, the ship was a roll-on/roll-off (Ro/Ro) vessel designed to carry many types of vehicles on its multiple cargo decks. GTS stood for Gas Turbine Ship.

yet another unusual and adventurous assignment. However, since the GTS Callaghan assignment was still months away, in the interim I was the "next man up" for another project that would ultimately open even more new opportunities. Of course I had no idea of the ramifications at the time.

In stark contrast to the international ship assignment, which would send me to Europe for the first time ever, my next assignment was literally less than one-half mile across the Schenectady plant campus. While the assignment seemed mundane, involving data acquisition, processing and analysis what really intrigued me was that the work involved GE's Industrial Gas Turbine Division[15].

During the mid-1970's, GE was manufacturing smaller size industrial gas turbines (under about 35MW) at the Schenectady plant (primarily Buildings 49 and 53). Larger gas turbines were being manufactured in GE's newly constructed Greenville, South Carolina facility[16]. Component development and testing, particularly for combustion hardware, for all GE Heavy Duty gas turbine products, was being performed in Schenectady's Building (262) known as the Gas Turbine Development Lab (GTDL)[17]. My assignment was to the GTDL where several of my Measurement Services colleagues were already helping to assist on component measurements and data reduction/analysis supporting GE's fast-growing gas turbine business. Later that summer, I was also temporarily assigned to support testing and measurements at the Greenville, South Carolina facility.

In the world of large industrial gas turbines, GE was a major global player. GE initially entered the industrial gas turbine business in the late 1940's with relatively small industrial turbines, leveraging expertise gained from prior military jet engine experience. Early industrial gas turbines were used in a variety of applications from train propulsion, to mechanical pump

---

15 GE was also in the primarily land based Heavy Duty industrial gas turbine business. Smaller versions of the Heavy Duty Units were also used in marine propulsion applications.

16 During this period GE was building smaller industrial gas turbines (MS3000, MS5000 and MS6000) in the Schenectady, New York plant and the larger units (MS7000 and MS9000) in the Greenville, South Carolina facility.

17 The GTDL had many unique and specialized test capabilities including single burner test stands for each model gas turbine capable of operation at full operating pressure, temperature and flow, metallurgical specimen ovens, "cold" flow and spray test booths for fuel nozzles; and a spin pit, also called a "wheel box", which could draw a vacuum to allow for spin testing of various instrumented rotor components.

drives, eventually expanding into marine propulsion and ultimately applied to electric power generation. As technology progressed, gas turbine units grew in output capability paving the way toward very large generator drive units in stationary applications. During the mid-1970's GE introduced what was then its largest 60 Hz gas turbine model (nominally rated about 70MW), known as the MS7000 series[18]. GE had designed and built the MS7000 as a scale-up from the smaller, but very successful, MS5000 gas turbines. Technical, environmental regulatory issues, and even scaling problems, all created challenges for the newly introduced MS7000 units. Problems meant there was abundant need for test engineering, measurements, data reduction and analyses which in turn created needs our Measurements group fulfilled. It certainly was a boom time for the Measurement Services team, as it rapidly expanded to meet growing demands from both internal GE businesses and external customers alike.

The GTDL was really a fascinating learning facility for me. In the summer of 1976, the Measurement Services group grew rapidly. I would estimate we numbered about a dozen engineers along with half that many skilled technicians. Perhaps three or four of us were assigned to support work in the GTDL or the Greenville facility.

During this time I became involved in a number of activities ranging from instrumentation, where I actually applied, calibrated and collected data from thermocouples, dynamic strain and pressure gauges. I learned to operate FFT (Fast Fourier Transform) machines converting time based measurements to the frequency domain for further analysis. It certainly was terrific to actually be applying some of the theoretical math and hands on lab experimentation techniques I studied during college in such a practical manner. Once again I was pleased to see that much of the advanced electronics at the GTDL was Hewlett Packard (HP) equipment. HP seemed to have some of the best, most "engineer friendly" products at that time. I certainly developed a preference for their logic, ease-of-use and reliability. Once again my prior experiences at SIS (from my Co-Op assignments) proved very valuable as I was already quite familiar with HP electronics and managed to quickly master use of new HP devices.

While supporting testing and data reduction at the Gas Turbine Development Lab, I especially gained exposure to virtually every gas turbine hot

---

18 MS nomenclature meant Model Series

gas path part. Fuel nozzles, combustion liners, flow sleeves, transition pieces, turbine nozzles and buckets all underwent testing in this facility. Along with the hardware, each day seemed to introduce me to new and interesting GE people, which was always fascinating in itself.

One of the most memorable folks I encountered at GTDL was a seasoned technologist named Norm Montague. For some unknown reason Norm and I seemed to naturally gravitate to one another. Soon we discovered that I knew Norm's oldest son, Tom, when we were classmates for a year in high school. From that point on, Norm adopted me just like another son, and I was immediately taken under his personal stewardship.

Norm was a treasure trove of technical information, hands-on experience and keen insights about how things "really get done in GE". I truly loved and respected Norm, both the human being and the technical expert, as much as anyone I worked with at GE. He shared so much knowledge and introduced me to all the right folks, constantly giving me pointers on things to watch out for.

I received personalized, hands-on instructions for tack welding thermocouples and dynamic strain gauges on turbine parts. Norm wanted me to not only understand the data, but everything about where that data came from including problems, biases or premature failures that could result from improper instrument installation. Norm helped me dig deeply into just about everything I worked on. I'll be forever grateful for his tutoring, which taught me so much.

Later that summer, when I was sent to Greenville, South Carolina, it was Norm who provided me with maps, recommended hotel accommodations, restaurants and even the local rental car agency that provided top line autos and free airport delivery/drop off for GE employees with minimal hassles.

Norm was way more than just a technical expert. He also knew how to have fun. Some colleagues said he resembled the cartoon character, Yosemite Sam, perhaps because of his build and full reddish beard. Well I suppose in some ways he did. The ever-jovial Norm seemed to enjoy the pun and would sometimes mimic his animated self by muttering to the group, "Ya'll get over here right now you ornery rascals".

Not only did he recruit me to the GTDL softball team, but he took me skeet shooting at his club, helped me tune our then popular CB radio antennas and generally shared a wide variety of fun times. Norm continued to be a friend and mentor to me for several years as my career progressed. Sadly Norm contracted cancer and passed away very prematurely. I want to acknowledge Norm again here and thank him for all he did for me.

During the summer of 1976 I completed my first gas turbine tour of duty in both Schenectady and later another assignment in the Greenville facility. Greenville gave me the tremendous opportunity to see the largest gas turbines GE was producing in all stages of assembly on the factory floor. Further, I was able to assist with testing fully assembled units in the "Test Building" at Greenville. It was an eye-opening opportunity and I just had a wonderful time with the gas turbine folks. I began forming long term friendships that would continue on for many years. My relatively brief exposure to GE's Gas Turbine Engineering and Test world certainly stirred something deep in me that left me yearning for more. These feelings would fester as I was recalled to prepare for the Callaghan assignment.

The constant shuffling from job to job was beginning to take a toll on some of my associates. Some were already becoming disenchanted by our leader DK who was virtually singularly focused on "renting" each of us[19] to maximize earnings for the growing Measurement Services business. Our manager did not seem at all concerned with individual skill development, job satisfaction, or career planning, but seemed singularly focused on maximizing services revenue. Assignments were randomly being made, to the "next person up" regardless of training, ability or personal preferences. People were being "thrown in", relocated and re-assigned multiple times and simply expected to "adjust" in a constant shuffle of people and assignments. Certainly this was not an ideal situation as we all had different skill sets, backgrounds, experience levels and personal preferences. Although I sensed the discontent from many of my co-workers, at the time my attention was mostly on meeting many new people and understanding the new technologies constantly coming my way. Little did I realize that I too was on a collision path with DK just a few short months down the road.

---

19 Among SIS Engineers on the team we began sarcastically referring to ourselves as "Rental Engineers" or "Rent-An-Engineer".

— *Chapter 4* —

ANCHORS AWAY

IN LATE SUMMER 1976, I was notified the GTS Callaghan would be arriving in Norfolk, Virginia, following a special mission transporting helicopters to the Mediterranean in support of a military search effort.[20] My instructions were to meet the ship, along with some GE personnel from Evendale[21], Ohio, at the large US Naval base in Norfolk.

I arrived at the base driving a shiny new white rental Monte Carlo. After carefully examining my GE identification, the gate MPs directed me to park adjacent to where the Callaghan was docked. Leaving my car, I was awed by a convoy of helicopters being unloaded from the ship. The main rotors of each craft had been folded and fastened by cables to the tail, allowing for easier transport and more compact storage. Now, the helicopters were being towed down the Callaghan's aft ramp and moved to a field area alongside my parking area. In the field, other military personnel were unfolding the large rotors and preparing the choppers for flight. Awaiting pilots were quickly starting and flying the readied helicopters to another part of the base. Overall, it was a most surreal scene that caused me to pause and simply observe how smoothly this complex choreography was being executed.

As I stood watching, mesmerized, a handful of other civilians approached. They turned out to be the Evendale GE colleagues I was to meet. As we exchanged introductions, they expressed their amazement that I was given permission to park so close, when they had been instructed to park much farther away. Perhaps my newer, sportier rental car earned me a more favorable parking spot from the MPs?

Most of the Evendale personnel were regularly assigned to monitor and maintain the Callaghan's GE engines whenever the ship docked state-

---

20 My recollection is that the search involved a lost nuclear weapon in the Mediterranean.

21 Evendale is a northern suburb of Cincinnati where GE has a large Aviation engine plant. This is the plant where the LM2500 was manufactured.

side. The lead engineer for the Callaghan measurement project was an experienced engineer named Bob who had been specially selected to lead measurement efforts.

In just a short introductory conversation, it quickly became apparent to me that Bob indeed was quite knowledgeable in air sampling measurements. However, I also sensed that this shipboard application presented a new and unique situation.

To my knowledge, such an engine inlet sodium measurement system had never been used on a ship before. Therefore, Bob and I would essentially be constructing a custom sampling system from scratch. Calibration and testing procedures would need to be developed and refined using Bob's extensive experience as a guide. I felt most fortunate that I was in on the ground floor of this project. Hands-on fabrication and check-out of the system would give me a much better understanding of how everything worked. Such a unique situation also afforded me an amazing learning opportunity and hopefully also would allow me to contribute my own ideas.

Once logistics were completed with an on-duty crew member[22], we were cleared to bring our equipment on board. Since I had secured such a great parking location, Bob and the others asked to use my rental car to help transport our equipment and heavy tools closer to the ship. Even better, a Callaghan crew member suggested that I actually drive the car on board to minimize our hauling efforts. Of course, I was warned to keep clear and yield to the on-going helicopter unloading activity.

The thoughtful suggestion certainly was a major work saver and immediately gained me favor with my new associates. After driving my fully loaded vehicle up the aft ramp, we discovered a convenient nearby stairway leading directly to the test trailer deck. Further on, there also was access to another stairway leading directly to the engine room, one level below the trailer.

I had never before been aboard any large seagoing vessel, so I was most impressed by the GTS Admiral Callaghan. To think I would be making my first international trip aboard this ship was astonishing. Before anyone gets any misconceptions here, let me be very clear: The Callaghan would never be mistaken for a luxury cruise liner. The vessel was essentially a giant multilevel floating parking lot, and living accommodations were far from lavish.

22 The Callaghan was manned by a Merchant Marine crew.

The ship was designed primarily to carry a merchant marine crew (about 10 officers and 20 seamen) along with many types of vehicles, including tanks, Jeeps, transport trucks and even automobiles[23].

All vehicles, or any cargo for that matter, needed to be securely fastened to the steel decks by sturdy cables equipped with adjustable turnbuckles and hooks. One end of each cable would be attached to the vehicle or cargo and the other end ran to four-point star-like cut-outs located every few feet on the Callaghan's metal decks. Typically, each vehicle would have a minimum of four cables securing it to the deck. Heavier equipment, like tanks and larger trucks, usually had more cables. Once the cables were attached, they were tightened by skilled loaders and checked periodically by crew members during the voyage. I didn't fully appreciate all of the cabling until I actually experienced ship gyrations caused by heavy seas. More about this later.

Nearly 700 feet in length, the Callaghan had multiple deck levels (three main decks as I recall) that were each interconnected by ramps similar to those in large multilevel, land-based, concrete parking facilities. I learned that this type of ship was called a Ro/Ro Ship (short for roll-on/roll-off) in reference to vehicle cargo. Vehicles literally would be driven on and off either via the aft ramp or a number of side ramps, depending on dock configuration.

Atop the aft portion of the vessel was a superstructure that housed very mundane living quarters including individual rooms, kitchen, mess and the like. At the very top of the superstructure was the bridge, which by my estimate was some 10 stories above the water level. I was most fascinated by the bridge and would spend much of my "off" time there, interacting with ship officers. My hours with officers on the bridge were extremely interesting, and I enjoyed privileged officer status[24] while on board. During my sea adventures, I gained tremendous on-the-job merchant marine education in ocean navigation, communication and overall ship operation.

My assigned quarters on the Callaghan were located just one deck below the bridge, on the same level as the captain, first mate and chief engineer. While my quarters were convenient to the bridge, they were quite some dis-

23 Trips from the US typically transported new military equipment to Europe. Return trips included retired military vehicles and often European automobiles purchased by military personnel returning stateside.

24 Aboard the Callaghan I was given "officer status" with respect to quarters, mess, ship access, etc. As a GE Engineer (contractor), I reported to the ship's Chief Engineer.

tance, perhaps a hundred vertical feet or more, to the GE equipment trailer, located far below, just one level above the engines themselves. The circuitous path, down multiple stairways, through hatches and sometimes ladders, provided plenty of daily exercise just "commuting" between my quarters and the GE trailer.

My room location directly under the bridge meant I needed to shade my room's only tiny window in the evenings to avoid any external light "leakage." At night, only the low glow of instrument lights and special low level red lighting was used for bridge illumination to preserve the crew's night vision. At night on ships crews are constantly visually scanning the vicinity on watch for other traffic in the darkness.

The lower portion of the superstructure housed more crew quarters and also provided inside access, via stairways and ladders, to all the lower decks, including the GE instrument trailer deck. Forward of the superstructure, on the Callaghan's main deck, there was space for additional cargo or vehicle storage. Unlike in the lower holds, cargo stored on the main deck would be directly exposed to the weather, including wind driven ocean spray, and giant waves. The Callaghan's main deck also was equipped with a number of boom cranes and associated cabling. Deck cranes could be used to on/off load cargo when dockside cranes were not available.

Two GE LM2500 engines, one for each propeller shaft, provided impressive propulsion power for the ship. In fact, I learned that the Callaghan was one of the fastest ships in its class during the 1970s. The main focus of my duties, these engines—one on the port side and one on the starboard side, coinciding with each of the Callaghan's two propeller shafts—were housed in separate compartments deep within the lower aft portion of the ship. Aboard ship, the engine room was typically referred to as "Engineering," presumably because the ship's engineers were responsible for propulsion, among many other duties.

Each engine drew intake air through an aft-facing inlet filtration system mounted high in the superstructure. Hot exhaust gases flowed through separate stacks located more forward, still higher in the superstructure than the inlet. Keeping the hot exhaust discharge higher than the inlet helped prevent unwanted recirculation of hot exhaust gases. I presumed the aft-facing inlet location was an attempt to minimize salt spray ingestion as the ship made its way across rough seas. To properly align with the above duct configuration, the Callaghan's engines were mounted backwards, with compressor inlets facing aft.

One deck above the engine room, but still below the Callaghan's water line, was the GE instrumentation trailer where our measurements took place. The standard 32-foot by 8-foot trailer sat between the two inlet ducts as they ran vertically through the ship. Like any other cargo, the trailer was properly lashed down to the deck as well.

Inside the trailer were hard-mounted racks crammed with electronics to monitor and record engine data. At the forward end of the trailer was a flat table that spanned the trailer's full width. The table would become our primary work space for installing and operating the sodium monitoring equipment. Like the trailer itself, and all other cargo, everything within the trailer was hard mounted and firmly secured to prevent unwanted movement in response to the inevitable motion of the ship.

Measuring sodium levels at the inlet of each engine required us to run two separate sampling probes, one for each engine. The actual sampling points would be from each inlet air duct adjacent to the trailer. The sample location was perhaps 15 to 20 feet upstream of the LM2500 compressor inlets. Two separate isokinetic[25] sampling probes, one in the port and one in the starboard engine inlet duct, were to be used. Flexible stainless hoses ran from the probes to the trailer. The flex hoses allowed us to move the probes to various locations across the duct to validate representative sampling locations.

Inside the trailer, we transitioned to stainless tubing, equipped with manual valves tied to a common header, where we selected samples from either the port or starboard engine. The sampling system required installation of many feet of stainless tubing, valves, gauges and fittings. Although this was the first time I had worked with stainless tubing and compression fittings, I quickly became adept at the task.

A very specialized sodium analyzer, built by a company called Moore, was used for these measurements. The analyzer used chemiluminescent light emission from a flame to detect, and ultimately quantify, sodium levels. This particular analyzer required a hydrogen flame for the sodium measure-

---

25 With isokinetic sampling, we did not change the velocity (kinetic energy) of particles we were sampling.

ment, presenting an interesting dilemma since the US Coast Guard would not allow storage of flammable hydrogen bottles below the ship's water line. Somehow, the Evendale team convinced the US Coast Guard to approve use of hydrogen generators, which created an on-line hydrogen supply from electrolysis of distilled water. As an additional precaution, once our daily measurements were concluded, we followed a strict procedure, shutting down the generators and then venting all hydrogen lines overboard. To take things one step further, once purging was complete, we re-pressurized the lines with inert nitrogen.

Once installed, we successfully calibrated and tested the measurement system on an overnight voyage from Norfolk to Bayonne, New Jersey. The Military Ocean Terminal in Bayonne was the normal US operations base for the Callaghan during the period I was affiliated with the ship. Military equipment was ferried between Bayonne and the port city of Bremerhaven, Germany in Europe.

When not working in the trailer, I was allowed access to the entire ship. On the bridge, which essentially is the nerve center of the vessel, I was wide-eyed watching the entire ship in full operation. Everything about the Callaghan was fascinating to me, and I constantly pelted the officers with questions.

The crew was most accommodating and seemed happy to have a curious young visitor on board. I met all of the Callaghan's mate officers[26] (first, second and third), who primarily handled shipboard operations from the bridge, including crew command, helm, navigation and other nautical duties. I also was introduced to the engineering chief and his first, second and third officers, who primarily monitored the engines and every other on-board system (including electrical, mechanical, hydraulic and water). The engineers, especially the chief engineer, were all briefed on our activities and would be carefully monitoring us to ensure we followed all safety procedures.

On the short voyage to Bayonne from Norfolk, I began to take note of potential dangers lurking throughout the ship. The transport of any cargo on ships always presents a danger, especially if it were to break loose under severe ship motion in rough ocean conditions. Being a very naïve seaman,

---

26 Both Bob and I formally met all of the officers and some of the crew. Our reclusive captain, also known as the ships master, was not very sociable and typically stayed in his quarters.

my knowledge was minimal in this area, but I needed to quickly get educated as we were about to begin our trans-Atlantic voyages. Although I had no formal safety training for any type of shipboard operation, my own instincts and awareness began to kick in. I began making notes to discuss with my boss upon my return to Schenectady. For instance, since I was expected to work alone aboard the Callaghan on future voyages, I thought it imperative that we have direct communication from our trailer to the bridge and engine room. To my surprise, no one had yet made those provisions.

Sailing into the New York harbor under the Verrazano Narrows Bridge, with the Statue of Liberty clearly visible in the distance, was extremely inspiring. My thoughts shifted to my grandparents, and so many other immigrants, who had sailed this very route long before me.

In Bayonne, the entire docking procedure was amazing to behold from the bridge. Each time a giant ship, such as the Callaghan, either enters or leaves a harbor, a licensed harbor pilot must come aboard and take command. Use of an experienced and qualified pilot greatly reduces the chance of mishap in congested or otherwise dangerous harbor areas that challenge the mobility of any large vessel. The pilot gives all maneuvering commands for the ship, and even commands the tug boats that typically assist moving the larger vessels.

After docking in Bayonne at the Military Ocean Terminal, the Callaghan began taking on board all types of military vehicles, including tanks, Jeeps, and personnel carriers. Vehicles were driven on board to a specific deck location based on calculated weight distributions to maintain appropriate weight and balance on the vessel. Every vehicle was lashed with cables and turnbuckles, to ensure each would stay in place during the inevitable motions of a ship at sea.

Holding cargo securely in place at all times was absolutely critical for obvious reasons, but the vehicles carried on Ro/Ro ships like the Callaghan present an additional problem. To expedite loading and unloading, each vehicle is driven via its own power, thereby requiring fuel in its tank. If a vehicle were to break free from its lashings, potentially contacting other vehicles or even the hull, fuel tanks could rupture and sparks could create a catastrophic fire. A loose vehicle could even puncture the hull, spelling serious trouble for a ship in heavy seas.

As time approached for our transatlantic departure, my excitement was building. Typically, voyages between New Jersey and Germany took about 10 days, depending on weather, specific routing and other factors. Allowing a couple of days for off-loading then re-loading, plus another 10 or so for the return trip meant my time away on any given voyage would be nearly a month. However, since the Callaghan had been re-routed to Norfolk, where I first came on board, that added almost another week to the transatlantic cycle. Once again, I was going to be out of the office for many weeks on end, only this time there would be no weekend's home in between.

Finally, our sailing day, or more accurately, our sailing evening arrived. For whatever reason, we were given a late evening departure slot. Once again, I found myself on the bridge, alongside the first officer and the New York harbor pilot. Again, I was fascinated to witness the radio chatter, bridge commands and resultant movement of both our ship and those of the assisting tugs from this special vantage point. As we proceeded, I caught one last glimpse of the Statue of Liberty glowing in the distance. I would experience a huge adventure before I would see that sight again.

Once at sea, life settled into steady shipboard routines that I hurriedly adapted to. Among these were multiple time changes that took place over the first few days, to keep in synch with various time zones as we traveled eastward across the Atlantic. It was everyone's individual responsibility to stay coordinated with official "ships time," as meals and other scheduled events, like emergency lifeboat drills, were scheduled on local time.

During the days, Bob and I took regular measurements, dutifully logging everything. As previously noted, my route to the GE instrument trailer, several levels below my quarters, required passage through multiple cargo decks. While at sea, the ship is constantly in motion, due to waves, winds, currents, and the engines themselves. Depending on weather conditions, both roll and pitch movement can be anywhere from mild to extreme. Below decks, in the cavernous, windowless and dimly lit holds, I walked alongside vehicles that were lashed in position by cables. The cable attachments, combined with the vehicles' own suspension systems, did allow some limited vertical motion as the ship pitched and rolled. The movement produced a very strange illusion that the vehicles were all dancing in unison to some unheard melody driven by unseen forces. No matter how many times I witnessed this phenomenon, even though I understood the underlying physics, it always created a very spooky and unsettling feeling.

Days at sea, far from land, can become monotonous. Usually there is not much of anything but water in every direction as far as the eye can see. All of this was a new experience for me. Still, I was full of curiosity, taking every opportunity to explore this new world I found myself in. The mates, engineers and even the radio officer seemed happy to accommodate my endless questions as they explained details about navigation, course charting and many other nautical procedures.

In the evenings, I headed up to the bridge to track our progress and continue to learn more about maritime operations. One evening, in the mid-Atlantic, the first officer invited me to "take the helm" for perhaps 10 minutes. We executed some gentle turns so I could get the "feel" of steering such a giant vessel. It was an amazing experience! How many 22-year-olds get to "drive" a 700-foot ship powered by two 20,000-plus horsepower "jet" engines?

Navigation across such vast transoceanic distances, seemed very intriguing to me. In the mid-1970s when fairly close to land, the crew demonstrated use of an older electronic navigation system called LORAN (short for Long Range Navigation). Position was established via straightforward triangulation from three radio beacons. LORAN had a number of shortcomings, including weather interference, so I suspect it since has been supplanted by other more modern means, such as satellite navigation.

On clear days and nights, I was amazed to learn the crew still used a sextant to establish our position via sun or star readings. Apparently, this "ancient" technology continues to be quite useful, especially as a cross check on electronic navigation tools. Although I attempted to take a couple of sextant readings, I was not successful, as I couldn't properly keep my target star in view due to the constant rolling of the ship.

Traveling by sea, I gained an appreciation of how huge the world is. Despite traveling at more than 20 knots, we saw nothing but water in every direction for days on end. Conversely, I experienced how small we were, including our nearly 700-foot-long ship, which was a mere spec in the massive Atlantic Ocean.

When working aboard a ship, days of the week, holidays or any other event measured by calendars simply don't matter. Every day is a work day requiring each person to perform a job, maintain equipment, cook meals, and navigate to ensure our tiny floating world makes it safely across a vast ocean. On the Callaghan, crew members worked two four-hour shifts, each followed by eight hours off. For example, if you worked 8 to 12, you worked that duty cycle both in the morning and the evening. While I tried to maintain a normal eight-hour work day, this wasn't very practical, so I just worked as needed to get the job done.

As I spoke with officers, I learned that they typically worked three-month duty tours. During the "off" months, the ship still operated, but with a second crew. Compensation for the ship's crews were commensurate with the long hours they worked and recognized that they were effectively away for continuous three-month periods. In sharp contrast, I was only being paid my standard salary, nominally based on eight-hour days, five days per week, with standard time on weekends. Something needed to be rectified here. More notes were added to my growing list of concerns for discussion with my boss upon my return.

In addition to the dangers previously cited, there were other dangers just moving about the ship. Basically, there was an "inside" and an "outside" multi-level route from my quarters to the trailer. Either route required climbing up and down many stairs[27] and passage through multiple water-tight steel-hinged hatch doors. Just keeping my balance was tricky on a rolling, pitching ship. Outdoor steps, even with hand rails, subjected me to stiff winds and rain-slicked surfaces.

Simply opening a water-tight hatch was a challenge on a rolling ship. Normally—in the horizontal, non-moving world—most of the weight of any door is on the hinges. On a rolling, pitching ship, if you open a hatch at the wrong time, gravity and vectors can quickly work against you, resulting in the transfer of a huge portion of the hatch weight against your body. In fact, the force can be so great, one can be seriously injured or crushed by this load. On a ship, you quickly learn to carefully coordinate passage through any steel hatch to occur at a time when the ship is in a fairly level position. Probably any sailors reading this are smiling, as I'm sure they learned this lesson very early on. But remember, I was an un-

---

27 On board, we had an aircraft altimeter that we used as a very sensitive pressure gauge. I carried that altimeter from the bridge to the trailer one day and measured over a 100-foot vertical change in elevation!

trained 22-year-old on my first ocean voyage, so I had to rapidly master many lessons of seamanship 101.

During my first crossing, in the fall of 1976, the north Atlantic was relatively calm. That was good, because all my senses were being bombarded with new experiences. However, my views about this "great sea adventure" quickly changed on the very next voyage when a severe storm stalked us for days, making for a most uncomfortable and unsettling trip.

In addition to the sodium measurements, I was asked to program a data scanner, also located in our trailer, to capture periodic engine readings to correlate with our sampling data. The scans also recorded much needed data for the performance team back in Evendale. By sheer coincidence, the scanner was made by my favorite electronic manufacturer, Hewlett Packard. Already familiar with other HP equipment, I promptly mastered this task.

Approaching Germany, the Callaghan sailed down the Weser River and then through a lock to our dock in Bremerhaven. With the ship safely tied to the pier, I looked forward to setting foot in Europe for the very first time. But before disembarking, yet another task was added to my duty list. Upon each European arrival[28], the Evendale team asked me to take water wash samples from each engine. I needed to coordinate this task with the ship's engineers, since I had to manually operate valves on the engine during the washing procedure to collect the samples.

Here, things got interesting. To collect the wash water samples in quart-size plastic bottles, I had to be right up against the engine itself to operate a small manual drain valve. Of course, I wore coveralls, plus eye and hearing protection when doing this. But I must say this procedure was, initially, more than a bit unsettling.

Here I was right next to this turbine as the starting motor spun the rotor. Even with ear protection, I still could hear the unmistakable whine of a jet engine spooling up to speed. Now, however, there was the added sensation of "feeling" the vibration from this powerful machine as I leaned against engine supports to obtain the water samples. Although the process eventually became fairly routine, the experience never failed to get my adrenalin flowing.

---

28 During the stateside arrivals, the Evendale performance folks would be available to take the wash samples.

Once I set foot in Europe I was anxious to explore Bremerhaven. I hit some local sites and restaurants recommended by the crew. I also looked forward to enjoying a good sleep in a stationary bed, not subject to constant motion as aboard ship.

After two quick nights in Bremerhaven, I re-boarded the Callaghan as the ship's crew prepared for the return voyage. I was looking forward to returning home to share my experiences with family, friends and co-workers. Unknown to me at the time was the fact that our seldom-seen ships master (i.e., the captain) also was looking forward to a well-earned retirement upon the completion of this final trip. Certainly, neither of us was prepared for the unwelcome excitement that was only hours away.

As we sailed into the English Channel on our return trip to the US, the Callaghan experienced a catastrophic failure of our main hydraulic system, which controlled the rudder. Although we were not yet in the narrowest portion of the Channel, we still were in a very precarious situation. The English Channel is always a very busy shipping lane. Commercial and/or military vessels transiting this area must maintain precise headings and speed to avoid collisions, even in the best of weather.

As fate would have it, when the failure occurred I was in one of my favorite locations, standing on the bridge looking out the forward windows, directly in front of the captain's chair. I sensed something amiss when the helmsman called out to the on-duty bridge officer saying he had no helm response as he struggled to maintain heading. The seas were somewhat choppy that day as high winds were blowing and visibility was not great. Immediately, the bridge called engineering, and things began to escalate rapidly. Apparently, there was quite a serious situation down in engineering, where alarms were sounding and people were scrambling to determine what was going on.

The bridge duty officer next made a call directly to the captain and requested his immediate presence on the bridge. The officer then reduced speed as the crew struggled for control. Since the Callaghan was a twin screw (two-propeller shaft) ship, attempts also were made to regain some heading control by using the engines (one forward and one reverse), but the windy and rough sea conditions were not in our favor, and the ship continued to drift off course.

I sensed the mounting tension as I watched carefully and stood silently staring out the forward window. In the distance, I could see other vessels in our immediate vicinity. Before I could think further about the other vessels, two hands grabbed my shoulders. I don't think I'll ever forget the next words or tone I heard: "Get the hell off my bridge, NOW!" In a most unceremonious way, I had just been "introduced" to the previously unseen captain. Needless to say, I complied immediately, and headed to my room. Just my luck, a major incident on my very first transatlantic ocean voyage!

After my expulsion from the bridge, a number of emergency broadcasts were made, and within a short period all other shipping traffic in the channel knew of our position and situation. Eventually, two sea-going tug boats arrived and, in coordination with our crew, managed to get our ship turned around and headed back to Bremerhaven. We made it safely back, and the ship underwent a week of repairs, which afforded me additional time to explore northern Germany.

With the hydraulic system repaired, we resumed our return voyage, and this time made it safely through the English Channel. I even enjoyed a beautiful view as we passed the white cliffs of Dover. Bob and I continued to hone our sampling system routines and collected more inlet sodium data.

During my non-work hours, I enjoyed listening to discussions as the crew recounted the hydraulic failure episode. From what I learned, many heated exchanges took place between the Callaghan's crew, the ship's owners, and the faulty hydraulic equipment's manufacturer representatives. After all, such failures at sea were completely unacceptable. The entire event could have ended tragically, especially in the busy English Channel. On the return trip, our captain once again retreated to his quarters, and I never saw him again. I hope he finally got to enjoy a great retirement, despite the close call on his final voyage.

By the time I returned to the office, after my extended absence, I had developed quite a list of topics to discuss with my manager, DK. The most important items on my list were all safety related, particularly the need for communication in the trailer. Certainly, I was going to raise the topic of my compensation also now that I had a clearer picture of what the shipboard assignment entailed. Although there was another upcoming voyage over the Christmas and New Year's holidays, after such a long uninterrupted, isolated assignment, I felt I deserved to spend this important holiday time with my family. Little did I realize what a firestorm this meeting would create.

DK quickly agreed to improve my compensation. I would be paid for 12 hours each weekday (eight regular and four overtime) to account for my irregular work schedule plus the fact that I was on the ship 24 hours a day for weeks on end. On weekends and holidays at sea, I would be compensated at time-and-one-half for the entire 12-hour period[29].

However, following the compensation adjustment, I was shocked to discover that DK pushed back hard on my safety recommendations and further insisted that I cover the upcoming holiday voyage. Immediately, I was adamant about remedying the safety concerns, particularly the lack of any direct communication, before I would agree to work alone in the trailer. DK and I were at an impasse on that, plus he would not agree to allow me holiday time with my family.

DK finally confronted me with an ultimatum to either work the holiday trip, without implementing any safety improvements, or be fired. I left his office that evening without giving him a response. Just seven months into my GE career and I had progressed to a major impasse with my boss. Some serious contemplation was in order. Here, once again, fate took over. Within the next 36 hours, my issues with DK would be resolved, but not in a way that either of us could have expected.

On the very next day, I was directed to support a multi-day field trip to New York City to assist another Measurement Services engineer. Subway cars, known as GE's R-46 cars, were experiencing intermittent electrical blackout failures while in operation. No one could pinpoint a fault. One of my associates, named Dave, planned to install a continuous looping multichannel recorder to monitor key parameters and hopefully pinpoint the fault cause. Essentially, this was a simplified version of "black box" flight recorders used by most commercial airlines.

After a three-hour drive from Schenectady, we arrived at a subway train maintenance facility near LaGuardia airport and reviewed our installation plan with both the customer and the local GE representative. During the

---

29 Although I was a salaried professional, my salary was converted to an hourly equivalent for this type of assignment involving large numbers of work hours beyond a 40-hour week. This was typical for other professionals involved in such special projects. All others after me benefitted from my improved compensation negotiation.

review, we learned the train chosen for the "black box" test would not be available until later that evening, after the rush hour commute, so Dave and I checked into our rooms and had dinner.

At the appointed time, we returned with tools and equipment in hand. The "test" subway train was already parked on raised tracks mounted on concrete floors within the service facility. Under the train, between each rail, was about a 4-foot-deep maintenance trench that ran the length of the track segment inside the building. The trench allowed workers access to inspect and service the underside of each car. Happily, there was no electrified "third" rail within the building, as trains were "walked" into position using flexible power cables suspended from above.

With the train elevated on the floor rails, access inside the train cars was somewhat challenging. As I remember, Dave and I entered the cars via the end door at the forward end of the train, using a stirrup and hand grip. We had to straddle the edge of the pit as we stepped up onto the stirrup and pulled ourselves aboard.

Hours later, probably around 2 a.m., we had completed all we could do that first day. Since we were quite tired we called it a day planning to return the following day to complete our installation. Exiting the train by reversing the procedure used to board, I held the hand rail while extending my foot down to the stirrup. However, before my foot found the stirrup, I lost my grip on the hand rail and slipped, falling from the car. The very next thing I remember was staring up at the train from beneath. I attempted to focus as my brain tried to make sense of what my eyes were showing me.

I had fallen from the cab and was now lying in the maintenance trench under the subway train! While I was in no immediate pain, likely due to shock, I sensed moisture on the back of my neck. Apparently, I was bleeding from a gash I received in the fall.

People soon appeared to lend assistance and eventually bandaged my head. Others assisted in lifting me out of the trench, but there did not seem to be any means of transport. I remember being moved to a first aid station via wheel barrel or some type of equipment cart. Given the potential severity of a head injury, along with continued bleeding, it was decided that I should be taken to a local hospital emergency room. Dave suggested using the back of our station wagon for transport, so off we went under the direction of local workers in search of a nearby hospital. I have no explanation as to why no one called for paramedics.

At the hospital emergency entrance, we were stunned to find the doors locked and chained. Those with me began pounding on the glass and pulling on the chains, attracting the attention of an armed security guard who appeared with his weapon drawn. It just could not have been a more surreal sight. Fortunately, as other security personnel arrived, we were soon admitted to the emergency room.

Hours later, following negative X-rays and more than a dozen stitches to close the wound on the back of my head, I was released. Dave and I were able to return to our hotel rooms, just in time for sunrise. Unable to sleep, Dave decided to stay awake and contact the office to report the incident. I can just imagine the look on DK's face when he heard about my accident.

My guardian angel must have been with me again because I suffered no permanent long-term injuries from what could have been a catastrophic fall. Meanwhile, there were so many safety infractions associated with this incident that it could have been a training video on unsafe work practices. In my mind, lack of safety training and proper preparation and briefing prior to undertaking this job were key contributors.

Whatever the details surrounding the incident, DK was completely reluctant to accept any of it. In fact, fearing a stain on his business safety record, he was adamant that this would not be classified as a lost time accident! He was so engrossed in trying to manage the situation that he actually came to my home the next day and personally drove me into work. His reasoning was that if I just showed up in the office that day, he could record it as a work day and avoid reporting a lost time incident. To this day I don't know what was actually ever recorded, but I certainly never signed any time card that week. Whatever DK did, he did on his own.

On the upside, all of my previously ignored safety requests on the Callaghan were quickly approved. Since I was not medically cleared to assume full work duties, my holiday trip on the Callaghan was no longer a topic for discussion. Given the turn of events, even a callous person such as DK would have a difficult time justifying my termination now. So, as I recall, no one sailed on the Callaghan for that holiday voyage at the end of 1976.

Over the next months, I made two more North Atlantic crossings to Germany, each time training another GE team member, who ultimately completed the remaining data-gathering trips. Each of these trips had its own distinct experiences. Given time and space limitations, I shall record only one more here as it seems both curious and noteworthy[30].

On my final voyage, instead of sailing the normal route through the English Channel, the Navy routed us over the top of Scotland, through a passage known as the Pentland Firth[31], arriving into Germany via the Black Sea. This route was not often chosen, as it was a bit longer distance and the firth itself was somewhat of a nautical challenge. Even in good weather conditions, very strong tides and unusual currents, combined with passage between various islands, make precise navigation critical when transiting this region. Wreckage of many ill-fated voyages litter the sea bottom here. These factors all contribute to making the region a bit mysterious, somewhat like the Bermuda triangle.

As luck would have it, our transit of the Pentland Firth took place during daylight hours in fairly decent weather. During the passage I was again fortunate to be in my favorite spot on the Callaghan bridge. The first mate explained an unusual blip, painting each sweep of our navigation radar, was a coded signal from a specialized Racon buoy[32]. Such buoys are used to designate important hazardous locations, such as the firth, where positive buoy identification is crucial. Once identified, signals from this buoy confirmed a positive fix on our exact position allowing for safe transit through this tricky area. Yet another piece of interesting marine navigation trivia to ponder.

After many days at sea, spotting any land mass was a treat, and the firth lived up to its billing as a very peculiar region. During our transit we passed close to Scotland and several of the Orkney Islands. Here, even the dark blue/green ocean was remarkable. Giant swirls and eddies seemed to abound, keeping the helmsman intently occupied maintaining our course. Overhead, there was plenty of sea bird activity. I wished my old ornithologist buddy, Dr. Mike, could be here to help identify some of the more unusual sea birds

---

30 Many other interesting experiences occurred during my Callaghan voyages. Perhaps I'll consider writing a separate document sharing them.

31 Actually, the Pentland Firth is a strait separating the Orkney Islands from Caithness in the very northern-most reaches of Scotland.

32 Racon buoys are specialized electronically equipped buoys that periodically pulse out an electronic transponder code that positively can identify it using navigation charts.

that appeared. Whatever dangers were present, I felt the passage was an interesting diversion from the monotony of sailing on the open Atlantic.

Looking back, I believe the Callaghan project was extremely successful. Using our measurements and subsequent developments that sprang from that information, GE won many contracts for LM2500 engines in the US Navy and the navies of many allies. Even today, the LM2500 is one of the most widely used gas turbines for naval propulsion worldwide.

While neither I nor any of my colleagues ever received much recognition for the months spent working on the Callaghan, the experience was extremely valuable to me in many ways. Certainly I felt proud that I had, in some small way, personally contributed to the broader success of the LM2500. Beyond the technical knowledge gained, the overall experience built character and gave me confidence at a very early, yet critical stage, in my career. The project introduced me to people, places and equipment I never would have encountered otherwise.

At the conclusion of my final voyage, some Callaghan officers personally recognized and thanked me, presenting me with an impressive brass plaque labeled "First Class Engineer." I had the plaque mounted on a wooden holder and still have it today to remind me of my shipboard adventures.

Chapter 5

FEELING THE HEAT

RETURNING ONCE AGAIN TO MY HOME OFFICE in Schenectady after another Callaghan voyage, it was well into the spring of 1977, approaching my first-year anniversary with GE. In accordance with a newly initiated annual review process, GE required all professional employees to write up a summary of accomplishments over the past year. I had no shortage of projects to summarize in my ledger. Within my first year, assignments took me to five US states, plus to Germany three times.

To my astonishment, I learned that during my absence, my manager, DK, had moved on to a new position somewhere in the Midwest. No love lost there. Our relationship had definitely soured from the events of the prior December. Fortunately, the Callaghan assignment had kept me out of the office for much of the time, so DK and I rarely interacted after our December showdown.

Life was not so good for others on the team. A few of my associates had been fired following their own conflicts with DK. Still others sought out better opportunities and departed on their own, some moving on to the fast-growing Gas Turbine Division. I was keeping a close eye on Gas Turbine myself, following my service assignments there earlier.

A complete unknown to most of us, a fellow I'll call VS, was named manager of the Measurement Services Engineering group. VS had come from elsewhere in the company, but he seemed like a reasonable fellow. I did, of course, ponder what, if anything, had been passed along from DK, so to kick things off on a positive note, I proactively provided him with a summary of my first-year accomplishments.

VS assigned me to support a shock testing project for a large naval radar dish. Prior to installing such devices on ships, the Navy needed to verify that their gun directors would still function within specifications after various shock impacts, which simulated battle damage. Once again, I had landed another new and unusual project. Clearly, my learning did not end when I earned that engineering degree!

Almost hidden at the very back of the Schenectady plant was a large non-descript building that housed a large shock test stand. Up until this assignment, I didn't even realize that Building 258 existed. The shock stand itself consisted of a horizontal square steel platform, perhaps 8 feet on a side, mounted on large, industrial springs in all four corners. The springs attached the stand to a huge concrete cube perhaps 10 feet across per side. The cube sat in a square pit that was just deep enough to bring the top of the mounting platform to about floor level.

As I inspected the stand further, I noticed a large curved cast slot in the center of one side of the concrete cube. The slot was perhaps 3 feet wide and extended well into the giant concrete cube. Protruding out of the cube, on either side of the slot, were embedded steel I-beams that extended out perhaps 4-5 feet. The ends of the I-beams supported bearings and a round shaft from which a giant hammer was suspended. The hammer aligned perfectly with the slot opening between the I-beams. In fact, if the hammer was swung about its bearings, the slot arc provided an open area, under the shock stand, for the hammer to move freely. At the moment, the hammer hung idle from its bearings in an inverted vertical position, with head side end down.

Now I was getting the picture. When the hammer was rotated (lifted) away from the cube by an overhead crane and then suddenly released, gravity would accelerate the hammer and cause it to swing through the vertical position and up through the slot in the cube like a massive pendulum. At the top of the slot, the hammer then would strike an anvil-like target, vertically impacting the test platform from below. In this manner, substantial vertical shock "g" forces could be transmitted to both the stand plus any object firmly fixed to it. It was simple, yet clever and effective.

Over the next few days, two colleagues and I assisted with installation of the gun director and also developed a detailed instrumentation and test plan. Our work needed to comply with a military test standard, which to the best of my recollection was MIL S 901D. Luckily, one of my colleagues was an experienced senior engineer who previously had conducted this type of compliance testing.

The gun director itself resembled a large radar dish, set atop a pedestal or base, which housed servo motors to align the dish, accessories and associated electronics. Once the dish's entire assembly was mounted on the stand, we proceeded to install accelerometers and other sensors to measure actual "g" force levels, strains and additional test parameters. Next, we calibrated all sensors using real-time monitors and connected a data recorder to document results. Over the next couple of days we completed a number of shock impacts and the gun director contractor's demonstrated successful operation after each hit.

After successfully testing the gun director, we learned that our business had decided to exit the shock stand testing business. Therefore my associates and I were instructed to supervise complete disassembly and packaging of the stand itself, once the gun director was uninstalled. An Australian company had purchased the stand, so we needed to prepare to ship the massive equipment half way around the world.

During the disassembly, a professional heavy haul operator drove a large "low boy" trailer into the building to haul away the block, stand and hammer assemblies. Since the concrete block sat in a pit, it would need to be lifted out and placed on the heavy lift trailer. Lifting the concrete block, which weighed in the neighborhood of 70 tons, would push the rating limits of the building's overhead rail crane, which as I recall was something like 75 tons. Given the questionable safety factor involved, I don't believe such a lift would be allowed today. In any case the operators seemed comfortable attempting such a lift with the very old overhead crane installed in the building.

As the lift began, the massive concrete block slowly began rising from the pit. As the steel cables tightened and strained, they produced some wretched sounds—and things soon got really exciting. Two lifting cables running alongside the protruding steel beams began chafing against the beams and the imbalanced block began to tilt as it passed above the top of the pit. The I-beams acted as sharp knives and literally began to cut through the steel lifting cables! Suddenly, one of the cables failed.

The severed cable immediately began dissipating its considerable stored energy by whipping wildly from floor to ceiling as the giant concrete block rolled freely on its side, gouging the building floor adjacent to the pit.

Overhead, the bridge crane momentarily lifted off its support rails and bounced once or twice, as the stunned operator ducked for cover in his tiny cab.

For what seemed like several minutes, but was more likely 15 to 20 seconds, my associates and I watched incredulously as we cowered behind a large wooden crate. Our eyes wildly followed the swinging severed cable, which electrically arced against the exposed crane power lines each time they swung upward. Each electrical arc seemed to impart more energy to the cables, perpetuating further undulations.

Eventually, everything came to rest, and slowly we approached to assess the damage. To our amazement and relief, no one was injured. The block sustained only minor damage, including a slight bend on one of the hammer support beams. I'm not really sure if this incident ever got reported, but I suspect it did not. The "close call" was yet another example of poor safety awareness and precautions prevalent in the day. In sharp contrast with those days, today such a lift would never be attempted without qualified lift specialists, calculation reviews, signoffs and specialized supervision. Once again, I, as well as others, was lucky to have survived yet another episode that could have had a very different outcome.

I do have a post script on the transport of the crane to Australia: The ship transporting the block and hammer encountered a severe storm. Most certainly I can relate to ocean storms from my Callaghan days. During this particular storm, the hammer, which had been mounted on the open main deck of the cargo ship, broke free. Remember my previous words about securely lashing cargo? Today, the hammer now rests somewhere on the bottom of the Pacific Ocean. Hopefully the Australian shock stand customer was able to manufacture a new hammer from the drawings we provided.

Time marches on, and now it was almost two months past my first GE work anniversary, and still no word about my performance review or any mention of salary action. No doubt VS was still coming up to speed in his new role but, in my opinion, personnel issues should have been at the top of his list. I wondered what my review would be like, particularly given most of the managerial input would originate from prior manager DK. When I approached VS and asked him about this situation, he assured me he was "working it."

Meanwhile I learned of a Combustion Development Engineering position open with the Schenectady Gas Turbine division. I immediately contacted the hiring manager and expressed my interest. The position seemed ideal—a dedicated role working with gas turbines, which had captivated me since college. I was advised to officially "post" for the job and send over a resume. I did both, with hopes I would at least get an interview.

Of course, the world doesn't stand still, and in short order my next assignment loomed. I was headed to the auto capital of the US, Detroit, Michigan. Here, an important GE steel mill customer was having problems with one of its many large 5,000-horsepower electric motors. At this site, motor brushes on one particular motor were wearing at an abnormally fast rate and the customer wanted us to investigate and fix the problem.

My team had been contacted by GE's Detroit service shop, which served as the primary customer contact. One theory was that possibly the motor commutator was out of round so the shop inquired if we could check the motor commutator[33] concentricity. Never mind the fact that no one, at least in our office, had ever performed such a measurement before.

After some internal consulting, we developed a potential concept using an eddy current proximity probe. Eddy probes, or transducers, can measure the relative gap, or space, between the tip of the probe and a target surface. Probes come in various sizes, but the one we planned to use was approximately 3/8" diameter and perhaps about an inch in length. At SIS, I had used these relatively small cylindrical eddy current probes before. Our concept required mounting a probe in a specially designed fixture near the rotating commutator to check the gap during rotation. I was asked to design such a fixture, possibly using existing brush holders, so I put my imagination to work.

Fortunately for me, GE was still building these giant motors in our Schenectady plant. One afternoon I was allowed on the factory floor to closely inspect one. Seeing and touching an actual motor brush holder installed near the commutator really was infinitely better than studying crude two-dimensional drawings. In the three-dimensional world, I was able to envision, and then design, a simple fixture to both hold and adjust an eddy probe for this application. My fixture could be installed simply by removing a single brush holder and replacing it with my holder. To minimize any electrical problems, I had the fixture constructed from a non-conducting nylon material.

Once the fixture was built, I decided to rig up a small rotating model of the cylindrical copper commutator so I could test the entire setup in our lab prior to heading off to Detroit. I calibrated and practiced installing the probe in the miniature model that simulated the actual commutator. Careful cali-

---

33 Stationary brushes contact the motor via the rotating commutator to carry current to the windings.

bration was necessary because measurement signals from eddy current proximity probes changed, depending on target surface material. Probes typically
only produced linear signals, proportional to distance from a surface, over a
particular "gap" range specific to a given target surface material.

In this case, copper was the target surface material. Based on the sensor
specification, the probe I was using needed to be located between 5 and 30
mils (that's 0.005 to 0.030 of an inch) from the target surface. Such a tight
spacing constraint would make the planned measurements extremely challenging, to say the least. If, in fact, the commutator was a bit out-of-round (not perfectly circular), and the probe was mounted too closely, I could easily destroy
the probe while attempting the measurement. Too far away, and I would get
no useful data, as the gap would be beyond the probe's linear response range.
While I was short on experience, I was long on confidence! After completing
my bench testing, I headed to Detroit to attempt the actual measurement.

Aboard the flight, approaching Detroit's Metropolitan airport, our captain informed the passengers and crew that a warning light was indicating
the nose landing gear had not locked into position. After several attempts
to raise and lower the gear, the problem persisted. Next, we made a couple
of low, slow passes by the tower so observers could visually check the nose
gear, but nothing conclusive could be determined. In the end, the captain
made what was likely the smoothest landing I ever experienced. Emergency
personnel were fully deployed alongside the runway and followed us the
entire way as we taxied uneventfully to the gate. Apparently, the problem
was caused by a faulty indicator, but it sure made for much unwanted excitement. Little did I realize that the airplane flight into Detroit was a bit of an
omen on how this job would play out.

July in Detroit can be quite hot and humid, and the summer of 1977
was no exception. Inside a steel mill, air temperatures soar well above 100
degrees Fahrenheit, a tough welcome to the industrial world for a young engineer short on field experience. The local Detroit service shop introduced
me to the customer and, after a short meeting, we proceeded to the problematic motor. However, since it was mid-morning, with the mill in full production mode, I was not allowed to touch or even closely inspect the motor.

As I learned, the subject motor was one of several identical motors, all
arranged side-by-side with the drive shaft extending through a floor-to-ceil-

ing wall. On the opposite side of the wall was a conveyor that moved sheets of very hot stainless past a series of rollers driven by the motors. Each successive roller applied increasing pressure on the plates until they reached the desired thickness. It certainly was exhilarating to watch this process, despite the very uncomfortable air temperatures. I was asked to return to the factory in the evening, once the daily production run was complete.

Just to recount the situation, here I was, a 22-year-old, inexperienced engineer coming to work in an unfamiliar steel mill. Further, I was about to work on a giant 5,000-horsepower DC motor with almost no safety training whatsoever. Unfortunately, this lack of proper safety training was prevalent in the 1970s. If they existed at all in industrial work environments, safety procedures were often informal or impromptu, much like ad hoc laws in old "wild west" towns[34].

In any case, without thoughts of serious physical danger ever crossing my mind, I proceeded. About the only safety awareness I had stemmed from lessons my grandfather had instilled in me when helping with routine household electrical projects. His motto always was "safety first," and it possibly was only this innate sense of potential danger that kept me from harm. Primarily, I simply trusted those I was working with to look out for my safety. In hindsight, that was not a particularly good working mode. Abundant accident reports document serious injuries and fatalities, based on such poor assumptions.

At any rate, a second shift technician advised me that the motor was shut down for the night. Unaware of typical Lock-Out, Tag-Out procedures, I began working on the motor alongside the mill technician.

The cab over the motor's collector compartment, which housed the commutator and brushes, was about 6 feet tall, and the enclosure easily accommodated both the technician and me. Once inside the cab, we installed the probe, using my fixture, and then began a static calibration to set the probe in approximately the middle of what I had determined to be the linear detection range for copper. I conservatively mounted the probe even beyond its linear range to allow for some unexpected movement. If I didn't get a signal and the probe was intact, I could readjust to a closer setting on a subsequent attempt.

---

34 Under OSHA directives, GE and the industry as a whole since have implemented and greatly improved mandatory personnel safety equipment and training.

In the mid-1970s, the type of eddy current probe I was using was fairly expensive. The probe included an integral, electrically matched (calibrated), microdot connector wire that interfaced with a longer, more robust longer cable, which I connected to an oscilloscope and strip chart recorder. With everything now set, I was ready to commence testing. However, the motor wasn't scheduled for operation again until the morning shift. Now I was advised to return early the next morning when the production run would begin.

Early the next morning, I rechecked the equipment prior to the actual startup run, but as soon as I powered up my equipment, I realized the probe wasn't emitting a signal. I asked the first shift technician if we could inspect the probe, which was concerning since the motor was likely now "live." With the technician in the lead, I peered over his shoulder as he opened the access door. The problem was immediately revealed: The special calibrated microdot cable to my probe had been cut, rendering the sensor completely unusable! Just like that, a $400 probe was destroyed, and I didn't get a single data reading.

As we investigated this mishap, we discovered that the morning shift production supervisor, completely unaware of our special measurement activities, had made his rounds and noticed this strange wire attached to a production motor. Since this was an anomaly, he decided to remove the unusual wire to assure his motor would operate unimpeded for the upcoming production run. In a steel mill NOTHING stands in the way of a new production run.

A brief meeting was called to get everyone on the same page. Now, however, I needed a replacement probe. In hindsight, I probably should have planned on this. Anyway, I called Schenectady, and another probe was air shipped to me that very day.

Fast forward to my second measurement attempt. With the new probe in place and equipment once again ready, we started the test. I actually collected some preliminary data when the signal abruptly stopped. Once again we peered inside the enclosure. This time we observed that the wiring still was connected and intact. What could the problem be now? Whatever the issue, it needed to wait until shutdown, as no one could interrupt the production run.

That evening, when I was allowed to remove the probe, I was stunned to see that its entire face had been destroyed. How could this happen? Even though I had set the probe well away from the commutator surface (perhaps 40 mils), it still had come into contact with the commutator during operation. My only clue was that it happened after I began receiving some initial data. Either the commutator, supporting bearings, or possibly a combination of both triggered relative movement in such a way as to cause hard contact that destroyed the proximity sensor.

After several hours pondering this problem and multiple phone calls back to the office, we postulated that thermal expansion might be the issue here. Yes, that old textbook lesson about materials expanding as they get hot. Certainly, the copper commutator got quite warm under high current loading, so this could be a real possibility. Proceeding on this assumption, I made some quick calculations and ran them by the team back home. Once we all agreed on my nominal estimates, I readied for the next measurement attempt.

Once again, I needed a replacement probe, sent out by overnight air. I could just imagine the chatter back in the office. What the hell is this Davi guy doing out there? How many $400 probes has he destroyed? In any case, I had no choice but to press onward as another probe was express shipped to me.

The third try was the charm. My calculations proved pretty accurate, and I finally was able to acquire some good data on the commutator eccentricity. The data helped us verify that the commutator was fairly round and spinning concentrically. Under extreme loading, it slightly distorted, but not to a level that would explain the abnormal brush wear. What we did discover during our tests was, on that particular motor, many of the brushes were damaged or worn, plus a number had loose mechanical connections. As a result, there was a significant current imbalance among the various brushes. The brushes that still were in good mechanical contact were carrying much higher currents, causing higher local heating and excessive wear. Once the worn carbon brushes were replaced and brush holder connections tightened, the wear problem was greatly mitigated. Our end customer seemed pleased with the results.

Nearly 15 months had now elapsed since I began my professional GE career, and I couldn't have imagined a more unique or wider variety of assignments. In this book, it has taken five chapters to describe some of the highlights and challenges I experienced in this relatively short span. Now my career was poised to launch in a new trajectory. Countless new, unbelievable experiences and people were yet to come my way. Things were really about to ignite.

Chapter 6

PLAYING WITH FIRE

SHORTLY AFTER RETURNING FROM DETROIT, I was asked to interview for the combustion development position. It's hard to capture the excitement I felt about this break. Since my college days, I had felt a special passion for aircraft engines. While industrial gas turbines were not exactly aircraft engines, they were the closely related, larger industrial counterparts. In any case, GE was a leading world-class producer of industrial turbines. Working on them was a momentous prospect for me, and I decided to go all in to pursue this job.

Although I didn't have any "inside" contacts in GE's Gas Turbine division, I did feel a "connection" courtesy of prior multi-month assignments from my Measurement Services days. I vaguely knew hiring manager, Fred Wilhelm, but never had an extended conversation with him. To bolster my cause, I decided to bring along a copy of my RPI senior year jet engine design project. If nothing else, the document nicely summarized my gas turbine thermodynamic knowledge. Further, given the effort and long hours committed to completing the project, I felt it exemplified my willingness to work hard. Certainly, the A+ grade I had earned wouldn't hurt either.

GE's Gas Turbine division had a significant presence in Schenectady in the 1970s. The Engineering and Manufacturing offices were located in Building 53, a five-story reinforced concrete structure that approximately spanned the length of two football fields. The building appeared to be even larger because it was attached to a giant high bay brick and steel factory structure known as Building 49. Manufacturing for the MS3000, MS5000 and later the MS6000 series industrial units was conducted in Building 49. The larger MS7000 and MS9000 units were manufactured in GE's Greenville, South Carolina facility, a much newer and very modern plant that, unlike Schenectady, happened to be non-union.

I can't say if my jet engine design project was a pivotal factor, but the interview went very well, and I sensed a solid personal connection with Fred.

My good vibes were confirmed a few weeks later when he offered me a job with a respectable salary increase. A new door had been opened, and I felt my career was again moving forward. After overcoming an HR issue involving the eye-popping turnover rate from Services, including an extensive exit interview, I was eventually cleared to start my new role.

Unlike my non-existent training experience with Measurement Services, assimilation into the Gas Turbine division proceeded in a smooth, orderly fashion. Fred personally took time with me, one-on-one, as he introduced me to everyone, explained current issues, and outlined his recommendations for me to ramp up. Certainly, I had many questions. Fred wisely only provided selected answers, suggesting that I speak with teammates about remaining questions. Looking back, it was an excellent tactic to encourage interaction with the broader team, while also providing wider ranging views on complex issues.

The Combustion team basically consisted of two subgroups, designated as aerothermal and mechanical. A clever senior aerothermal colleague, a terrific British fellow named Bill, came up with a simple yet witty job description. According to Bill, the aerothermal team designed "holes", while the mechanical folks "figured out how to wrap metal around our holes." Put in slightly more scientific terms, the aerothermal team focused on fuel delivery, air distribution, gas flow patterns, dynamics, emissions and the like. Location, size and number of various air metering holes, along with fuel injection and flame stabilization, were primarily combustion aerothermal tasks. The mechanical team concerned itself with design integrity of hardware including manufacturing techniques, materials, mounting etc. While greatly simplified here, these tasks actually were quite daunting design challenges. My background, education and interests all aligned with the aerothermal side, and that's precisely where I landed.

Growing use of large gas turbines in the power generation industry made them a focal point for air emissions regulators. Ever lower emission levels were being mandated to control pollutants, particularly oxides of nitrogen or NOx (which is an abbreviation for NO and NO_2). As an industry leader, GE strategically was very proactive in the development of advanced emission control technology. The company committed many millions of investment dollars, resources and effort to this admirable cause.

In the mid-1970s, GE's Combustion teams concentrated efforts in two broad work areas. The first was addressing combustion hardware problems caused by internal combustion dynamic pressures that were detrimental to combustion hardware. The other was pioneering development of advanced Dry Low NOx (DLN)[35] combustion technology. Fred assigned me to work combustion hardware and dynamics issues[36]. Previous stints with Gas Turbine, as part of the Measurement Services instrumentation team, gave me a terrific head start in this area.

For GE, and the industry as a whole, combustion dynamics was a very challenging and complex subject area. Efforts focused on a fundamental understanding of dynamics, with dual objectives of reducing overall levels and making the hardware more robust. When I joined the Combustion division, GE was in triage mode, working MS7000 field issues. Increased usage of water or steam injection for emissions control was a contributing factor that exacerbated the dynamics problem. Diffusion flame combustors[37] used water or steam directly injected into the flame zone to reduce peak combustion temperatures. Lower peak temperatures helped minimize the interaction of nitrogen and oxygen to form NOx. Unfortunately, these diluents stimulated dynamic pressure fluctuations, which in turn damaged combustion hardware.

DLN development was its own distinct work area. Emissions control with DLN technology targeted NOx reduction without using diluents, hence the term "dry." Development of DLN would prove to be a much more difficult technology to master. The trick was to control air and fuel distributions, typically by premixing fuel and air before ignition. Premixing helped establish lean burning zones that reduced residence time at peak temperatures, thereby minimizing NOx production. Working closely alongside DLN teams afforded me an enviable vantage point to learn first-hand about

---

35 Dry Low NOx was terminology whereby oxides of nitrogen were controlled without the use of water or steam injection. The technology used lean burning combustion techniques to limit the formation of NOx.

36 When designing the MS7000 gas turbine, GE leveraged scaling from the smaller, very successful MS5000 units. While sound from a mechanical standpoint, scaling had inadvertently contributed to the combustion dynamics problem, particularly when water or steam was injected into the flame zone to control NOx emissions.

37 A diffusion combustor is where fuel and air immediately mix by diffusion and burn as they are coincidently introduced within the burner.

this cutting-edge technology. I had no idea at the time how instrumental this experience would be in future GE roles.

As a leading world-class company, GE was in the fortunate position to screen and select the most talented people it could find. Being selected to work among this elite group of employees on the Gas Turbine Engineering team was an honor. Once again, chance had landed me in the middle of some of the finest technical talent in a major division of GE. Time and space prevent me from mentioning all of these folks, but I will touch on a few along the way.

At the very top of the technical talent list is Dr. L. Berkley Davis, Jr., more commonly known to most as Berkley. The son of a GE vice president of the same name, Berkley was one of the most intelligent individuals I have ever met. His contributions to GE are legendary. Very early in his career, he revolutionized GE gas turbines when he developed what became known as the slot-cooled combustion liner[38], which eventually was incorporated in every liner in GE's product line[39]. His slot design efficiently routed cooling air exactly where it was needed along the liner wall, greatly improving convective heat transfer over the simple punched tab design it replaced. Precisely designed cooling holes, effectively located along the liner, metered just the right amount of air to each circumferential slot. Designers now had unprecedented ability to accurately direct precise cooling flows exactly where needed by adjusting slot length, location, cooling-hole diameter and quantity.

As a young engineer, Berkley had quickly established himself as one of the top technical minds in the business. Impressive as the slot-cooled liner was, it was only the first of many significant contributions he would make over a very long career.

There is no way to overstate how fortuitous it was for to me to have a person of Berkley's caliber to work with and learn from. He was a font of knowledge for me. Not only were we co-workers, but we developed a solid friendship that spanned my entire career. I always considered Berkley a close confidant and informal mentor as I often discussed my own career questions, problems and aspirations with him. I always had the utmost respect for his valuable, candid and beneficial advice.

---

38 Combustion liners in GE combustors essentially are specialized metal cylinders that help meter airflow and contain the flame.

39 While combustion liners have undergone many modifications, to the best of my knowledge, the slot-cooled technology is still used by GE today, more than 50 years after its introduction.

The Combustion assignment was transformational for me in other ways as well. First, I was directly responsible for key components of a world-class GE product. In addition, the role marked my initial exposure to long-term, complex problem-solving requiring years of concentrated effort and dedication by multi-disciplined cross functional teams. Finally, combustion also was where I first began regularly using computers as a tool to help solve complicated problems.

Horribly slow and painfully crude by contemporary standards, 1977-era computers were mainly remote time-sharing mainframes connected via problematic phone modems. In some situations, stacks of IBM punch cards were used as input media for computer runs. Recall, this was a period when dot matrix printers using ubiquitous white and green perforated paper driven through the printers via perforated holes on both sides.

Because of complex fluid dynamics, heat transfer and other factors, calculations using rudimentary computers of the time were not adequate for combustion design. Applying math, physics, chemistry and heat transfer could only get you so far. Recognizing this shortfall, in the early 1970s GE designed and built a state-of-the-art full-scale combustion test facility known as the Gas Turbine Development Lab (GTDL) located in Building 262 on the Schenectady campus. This facility was dedicated to gas turbine component testing[40]. Like most of my combustion associates, I considered the GTDL as a personal playground. Indeed, I was privileged to work there conducting tests. Not only was the lab extremely valuable for our combustion team, but it afforded GE a strategic advantage over competitors who had no such capability.

At the heart of the GTDL were several full-scale, single-chamber combustion test stands capable of full flow, pressure and temperature testing for the various GE Heavy Duty turbine models. Each stand could simulate design conditions for a specific turbine model, while dozens of sensors monitored a host of relevant engineering parameters that included dynamic pressures, metal temperatures, exhaust temperature profiles and emissions. Now this really was playing with fire!

The stands were operated from a central control room packed floor-to-ceiling with electronics to control, monitor and record data from combus-

---

40 Three primary GTDL component test areas were 1) metallurgy 2) rotor wheel box spin chamber and 3) gas turbine combustor testing. A second floor of Building 262 also housed an advanced Controls group along with an instrumentation/data reduction area.

tion testing. A skilled team of specialists manned various "stations" in the control room. The combustion development engineer was responsible for, and directed, all aspects of testing. Responsibilities included writing detailed test plans, modifying hardware, monitoring live data and making real-time decisions to continue or abort testing. Only months earlier, I had been a measurement engineer, monitoring and recording signals, under the direction of a combustion engineer. Now I was catapulted into being the lead combustion test engineer. Undoubtedly this was an awesome responsibility for anyone, but I always considered it a special privilege as a 23-year-old, working in this innovative facility. While my job was somewhat intimidating, maturity gained in prior roles, particularly on the Callaghan project, definitely helped bolster my confidence.

In the GTDL, two huge compressors, requiring about 2 MW of power, were needed to provide sufficient airflow to a single MS7000 test stand. Keep in mind that this stand simulates only one of 10 combustors on an actual machine! Such a large power consumption was expensive and significantly impacted the local power grid. Before starting a test, the lab was required to contact the plant load dispatcher to obtain permission from the local utility. To minimize expenses, while complying with local utility restrictions, we often conducted our testing in the dead of night, beginning around 3 a.m. and finishing up by 8 a.m. Operation beyond 8 a.m. incurred "peak demand" power charges for the entire test period, so every effort was made to finish testing by 8.

Things were going quite well when, only months into my combustion assignment, I learned that my manager, Fred, was being promoted into a new role. While that was great news for Fred, I was just getting "my feet on the ground" and suddenly I felt the ground shifting once again. Perhaps the previous experience with DK in my prior role was still in the back of my mind? In any case, the scenario of hiring into a job, only to have the person who hired me leave, would continue to haunt me several more times in my GE career, usually with not very pleasant results. I hoped for a better outcome this time.

Meanwhile I continued to build strong working relationships with my fellow Combustion colleagues as well as with GE engineers from other disciplines with whom we interfaced regularly. These included technologies like Materials, Rotors, Stators, Controls and Accessory Systems. Building long-term relationships with these talented folks would prove quite valuable throughout my career. I was especially lucky that many of my colleagues were also younger engineers like myself. Not only did we share a professional relationship at work, but many of us developed close personal friendships and regularly socialized outside of work, especially enjoying many years of sports activities including softball, flag football and pickup basketball. It was definitely a diverse and congenial group.

Much of my time in Combustion was dedicated to what became known as the Multi-nozzle, Quiet Combustor (MNQC), which was being developed for the MS7000 model. A very talented associate, Colin Wilkes, had developed the original MNQC concept. I took over Colin's design when he was assigned to the DLN program, and I completed additional development leading to a machine-ready prototype.

The MNQC concept replaced a single, centrally located fuel nozzle in each of the MS7001's 10 combustors, with six mini nozzles. Each of the six smaller nozzles were symmetrically arranged circumferentially at the forward end of the liner. From its earliest tests, right up through the first field machine prototype test, the dynamics were always low on the MNQC. Impressively, the dynamics remained low even as we injected high amounts of water or steam for NOx emissions control.

Over the years, we investigated many different concepts to replicate results of the MNQC, but found none worked as well. One success we did discover from laboratory testing was the ability to "tune" primary combustor dynamic "organ pipe" frequencies with geometry changes. In 1979, Berkley and I applied for, and eventually were granted, what became my very first GE patent. Titled "Acoustically Tuned Combustor," the patent was issued in 1983 following a strong rebuttal letter I wrote to the US Patent Office, which had initially rejected our application. I was now an official GE inventor[41], joining a long line that stemmed from our founder Thomas Edison!

When I graduated RPI with a BS degree, I suppose I thought that milestone event marked the end of my formal education. Nothing could have been further from reality. In fact, that first college degree was only the launching point of what would be, and still is today, a lifelong learning

---

41 Over my career I was named on 17 patent awards, with a number of additional applications still pending review when I retired.

process. Informally, I was constantly experiencing on-the-job learning from many talented colleagues. On a more formal basis, I was asked to consider joining GE's prestigious Advanced Engineering Course. After careful consideration, I instead opted to enroll in an Industrial Administration Master's degree program at Union College. My feeling was that the Union program, which was a core MBA curriculum, provided me broader future options. As time went on, that decision proved to be the correct.

Speaking of acquiring new skills, I also decided to pursue my long-time aviation passion and enrolled in flight training with our local fixed base operator (FBO) at the Schenectady County Airport. Months later, on a cold, calm and clear December morning in 1978, I completed my first solo flight, ironically on the 75th anniversary of the Wright brothers' first flight. It's quite difficult to describe the exhilaration I felt after piloting an airplane alone for the first time. Undeniably, I was jubilant—and would remain so that entire day.

On the day I soloed, I was wearing a three-piece suit in preparation for a GE technical presentation. Following multiple successful landings[42], in accordance with aviation tradition, my flight instructor cut my shirt tail. In his exuberance, he actually cut quite a bit more than just the tail from one of my best dress shirts. Material from that shirt was later sewn into wings that still hang today on a wall at the flight training facility. Berkley, himself a small aircraft pilot, shared in my excitement, especially after observing my ragged shirt tail.

As previously mentioned, the MS7000 (60 Hz model) gas turbine and the larger MS 9000 (50 Hz model) were manufactured in our Greenville facility. With most of Gas Turbine Engineering located in Schenectady, there was always a constant need for travel between these locations. At the time air travel between Greenville and our commercial airport at Albany, New York always required one and sometimes two stopovers, often making the trip a day-long event. One day I learned that GE had dedicated one of the corporate jets[43] to fly once-per-week round trips from Schenectady airport

---

42 Only after I was safely back on the ground did my young instructor reveal that I was only the second student pilot he ever soloed. Hard to say who actually was more nervous that day, but I was glad he waited until I safely completed my three required landings before informing me.

43 In the 1970s, GE had a fleet of mostly Falcon (7-8 passenger) corporate aircraft based downstate in White Plains, NY. Additionally I knew that GE also owned some larger aircraft, Gulfstream I (prop) and II (jet).

directly to Greenville. When a business travel need arose, particularly for a one-day trip, employees could request[44] a seat on the aircraft.

When my next Greenville travel opportunity arose, I contacted the executive administrator to our general manager and requested a seat on the corporate jet. I was elated to learn that there was a seat available. My instructions were to meet the plane at the Richmor FBO in Schenectady, the very same facility where I was taking my flight lessons. I was astonished at how easily the process worked.

With adrenaline flowing, I arrived early for "check in," which simply meant a manifest name identification check. Parked nearby on the ramp was a shiny Dassault Falcon jet[45]. I introduced myself to the two uniformed pilots and mentioned that I was taking flight lessons at this very facility. The revelation that I was a student pilot seemed to create an instant bond between us. When I asked permission to visit the cockpit while in flight, the captain casually invited me ride the entire flight in the "jump seat"[46]! Totally dumbfounded by his offer, I recovered enough from my momentary incredulity, to accept.

Corporate jet travel is great. There are no big crowds, and there is no boarding procedure. In short, there are no hassles at all. Once everyone arrives and is verified on manifest, you board and head non-stop to your destination. Riding in the "jump seat," I would be foregoing a plush leather seat, trading it instead for a much less comfortable, yet most enviable accommodation. It was a trade I would make any day.

Following the captain and first officer, I entered the tiny cockpit and strapped into the jump seat. The first officer handed me my own head set, including microphone, so we could all communicate more easily on the intercom system. Additionally, I would now be privy to all radio communication between our aircraft and air traffic controllers. Things were happening so quickly, I was having a difficult time comprehending this fantastic experience. Here I was, a 20-something engineer and student Cessna pilot, riding in the cockpit of a multi-million-dollar corporate jet with two professional pilots demonstrating their skills! Life just couldn't get any better than this. But it did.

---

44 Employee seating was offered on an availability basis. Company hierarchy dictated priority.

45 GE's Corporate Falcon 20 jets in the late 1970s were usually configured for seven passengers and two pilots. The jet had two rear fuselage-mounted GE (of course) engines allowing it to cruise at nearly 500 mph at altitudes up to about 40,000 feet.

46 This is a folding seat located just behind the center console between the pilot and first officer.

As an observer on the flight deck, I planned to simply sit, listen and observe. I was completely respectful of the privilege that I had been given. Absolutely the last thing I wanted to do was disturb the two professionals who had been so gracious as to allow me in their cockpit. After all, it was their responsibility to get all of us to Greenville safely.

My seat was on the aircraft centerline, directly between and just aft of the captain and first officer. The center console, containing throttles, radios, and other flight controls, was just forward of my lap. As I recall, the jump seat was situated just a bit higher than the two pilot seats, so I had an excellent view out the forward windows. Never before had I been exposed to cockpit sights and sounds of such a sophisticated plane. It was incredible to watch these two pros operating this complex aircraft so effortlessly. Clearly, they were role models for my personal flight training.

It is hard to put into words a suitable description of that first spectacular takeoff. Here we were sitting at the end of the very runway I used many times while piloting my Cessna 152 training aircraft. And now here I was in the cockpit of a complex, multi-million-dollar Falcon business jet about to be launched into the sky in a way I would never forget.

Once the tower cleared us, the captain moved the throttles forward. My eyes constantly shifted between the numerous gauges now coming to life and the astounding view out the cockpit windshield. In seconds, we were airborne, and Schenectady tower quickly handed us off to Albany departure[47], and Air Traffic Control (ATC) radioed our instructions: "Falcon three, six, nine, Gulf, turn left heading one eight zero degrees, climb and maintain initial flight level one zero zero" (code for 10,000 ft.). Smoothly, our pilots executed the ATC commands and acknowledged the call.

This was so cool! I felt like part of the flight crew, listening to ATC clearances and watching two professional pilots effortlessly execute the instructions. In between air traffic radio calls, the first officer, who was handling communications on this leg[48], was explaining additional cockpit nuances to me. And, after engaging the autopilot, he began providing even more aircraft details to me.

---

47 Schenectady has no radar, so Albany handles all instrument flights via its radar-equipped approach and departure control zones.

48 Typically, one pilot has aircraft flight responsibility while the other handles the radio, navigation and other cockpit tasks.

Meanwhile, ATC merged us into other high-altitude traffic heading down the busy US East Coast corridor as we approached our 37,000-foot cruise altitude. Not lost in our exchange was a quick check of the engine instruments, in particular the fuel flow gauges. At 37,000 feet, I noticed the engines were burning fuel at about half the rate they had been when we held at 10,000 feet. While I had made similar theoretical calculations, this real-life experience meaningfully reinforced why jet aircraft operate at high altitude.

Flying nearly seven miles above the earth, it is difficult to get a full appreciation of travel speeds of nearly 500 miles per hour. In the cockpit at high altitude, however, I gained a more realistic perspective while observing opposing jet traffic and hearing the regular alerts of nearby traffic from ATC. Moments after such calls, the two pilots and I would spot contrails from an aircraft, hopefully at a different altitude and course. Opposing jet traffic provides a very dramatic visual speed reference as our combined closure rate is something close to 1,000 mph. A mere 2,000 vertical feet—and sometimes less horizontally—was all that separated us. Not much room for error here. Everyone on the flight deck gave this task due diligence.

While at cruise altitude, our first officer, whose name I can't recall, was quite talkative, describing the World War II exploits of the plane's captain. As it turns out, our captain was not just any captain. He was Captain James J. Farrell, then chief pilot for GE's entire corporate fleet! In World War II, as a young lieutenant, he had been an aviator commanding B-26 bombers flying missions from England to various European targets. Known by the handle, "Boss" by his B-26 crewmates, Farrell distinguished himself several times. On multiple occasions, he returned from missions after incurring heavy damage, twice with only one engine operating, yet still was able to somehow safely land his aircraft. The very man piloting the plane I was now flying aboard flew more B-26 Marauder missions than any other pilot during World War II! I was completely overwhelmed.

Farrell nicknamed his B-26 aircraft "Flak Bait" because of its tendency to attract more than its share of German antiaircraft fire. Later I learned the name originated from the family dog Farrell's brother called "Flea Bait." In honor of Farrell, his crewmates and the airplane, the fuselage nose section was displayed in the Smithsonian National Air and Space Museum in Washington, DC[49] for many years. As if the privilege of flying in the cockpit of a corporate jet was not enough, now I was astounded to learn I was in the presence of a truly great American hero.

Not long after I learned of his remarkable background, Captain Farrell executed a smooth "textbook" landing at Greenville, known by code identification GSP[50]. My prime cockpit seat literally provided a birds-eye forward view of the approach, glide slope descent and touchdown. This flight was one of the most fantastic experiences I have ever had!

I thanked both Captain Farrell and his first officer for the privilege of flying with them, even as enthusiasm was already building in anticipation of the return flight later that day. Safely on the ground in South Carolina, now I had to begin my workday—the real reason for my flight. Frankly, I don't think I ever came down to earth that day. While I can vividly remember so many details of the flight, I still can't recall the business purpose of my visit.

Sometimes when you are on good a roll, amazing things magically keep happening. As if on cue, the next wonderful experience occurred on the ramp just outside our aircraft. A beautiful young woman driving a shiny new sporty Olds Cutlass Supreme pulled up adjacent to the plane. She announced that she was from a local car rental agency and was looking for someone named Michael Davi. When I acknowledged, she popped the trunk and handed me the keys along with a pre-completed rental agreement[51]. Other passengers disembarking from our small jet stared in disbelief as they proceeded across the tarmac toward the Hertz counter. Thank you again, old friend Norm Montague, for cluing me in about that local car rental agency.

On the return trip later that same day, I once again rode the jump seat between Captain Farrell and his first officer. Others might characterize these as routines flights, but this was easily the most spectacular day of flying I've ever experienced. After landing back in Schenectady, I again thanked both pilots for the privilege. No amount of gratitude could possible express my feelings. Captain Farrell, I again thank you and salute you for your service to our country!

---

49 Months later, on a personal trip to Washington, DC I visited the National Air & Space Museum and located Captain Farrell's B-26 fuselage nose section. I have a photo of me standing next to it. Recently I learned there is an effort underway to restore the entire aircraft.

50 Pilots more commonly refer to this airport as Greer, which is a local town near the airport.

51 I had phoned my arrival information and identified myself as a prior GE client the prior day.

Months after that first cockpit trip to Greenville, I had another occasion to fly in a Falcon corporate jet. A different captain, David Stroup, also allowed me to repeat the honor[52] of riding the jump seat. For this trip, I had thought ahead and brought along my pilot log book, which Captain Stroup endorsed after the flight, using his official FAA-issued Air Transport Rating ID. Beside his signature he added a notation denoting the topics of cockpit familiarization and high-altitude navigation that we covered. When my Cessna flight instructor saw the entry, he was speechless. One of his students had logged cockpit jet experiences he still only dreamed of attaining! Like any good pilot, I still have my logbook. You never know when I might return to flying.

I made several other trips in corporate jets, one of which was in the newer, larger 14-passenger Gulfstream II, then one of the most advanced corporate jets around. Neither of those flights could accommodate me riding in the cockpit, as there was a third pilot occupying the seat, but they did allow me to visit the cockpit in flight. Such a blast! Flying in private jets point to point, in my opinion, is the only civil way to travel. You can keep all the long lines, crowded terminal gates, cramped seats, and hub changes. After my personal experiences, I now understand why corporate executives are so passionate and protective when it comes to their private jets. Corporate jet travel, for all but the most senior GE executives, ended abruptly when Jack Welch assumed the chairmanship. Glad that I had these unique experiences before the good times ended!

I must applaud GE for the many opportunities it afforded me to continually educate myself. The college tuition refund program was one of the most lucrative benefits I ever exercised. To all the young readers of this book, take advantage of whatever learning opportunities come your way, especially if they come with little or no cost to you! Dad's words continue to echo in my head – "No one can ever take an education away from you."

Never one to miss out on unique learning chances, I heard of one such chance from my very thoughtful Combustion associate, Colin Wilkes. Colin's favorite professor, Dr. Arthur H. Lefebvre, originally from Cranfield University in England, planned to teach a combustion course at Purdue University. Now head of Mechanical Engineering at Purdue, Lefebvre was an internation-

---

52 Perhaps Capt. Stroup accommodated me because I mentioned my earlier trip with chief pilot Capt. James Farrell?

ally renowned combustion expert. I, along with another colleague, was most fortunate to attend this prestigious week-long class in May 1979. In addition to working with GE's top talent, my sphere of exposure had now expanded to include one of the worlds' foremost experts. Absolutely remarkable!

Colin did not overstate accolades about his former teacher. Personable and entertaining, Lefebvre also was one of the finest instructors I ever had. Not only did I improve my understanding of gas turbines and combustion, but Lefebvre's presentations helped reinforce and clarify a host of topics I had previously learned, or thought I had learned.

Rarely have I known such an approachable professor as Dr. Lefebvre. The man actually took the time to pose for a photo with me outside the Mechanical Engineering building at Purdue, and I still have that memorable photo. His dinner talk on the final evening was both impactful and humorous. So profound was that course that I still remember it vividly to this day.

On the return trip from Purdue, as my associate and I made a connection at Chicago's O'Hare airport, we noticed a large group of flight attendants quietly gathered together, some hugging, while others appeared to be crying. While unusual, we didn't think much more about it. A short time later, aboard our Albany-bound flight, I happened to notice white foam on an adjacent taxiway and runway. I remember thinking to myself that there must have been a recent drill for the airport fire rescue folks. As we sat at the end of the runway just prior to takeoff, I noticed thick black smoke billowing skyward in the distance. Once again, I did not connect these observations.

As we deplaned in Albany, there was absolute bedlam in the arrival gate area. Reporters with microphones, bright lights and TV cameras immediately rushed toward me and the other deplaning passengers, asking if we had seen the crash. Crash, what crash? Suddenly all of the things I had noticed in Chicago jelled in my mind. I soon learned that one of the worst crashes in US aviation history had taken place in Chicago shortly before our flight had departed. American Airlines Flight 191, a wide-body DC10, crashed on May 25, 1979. Many of the people on that ill-fated flight had originated earlier from Albany, so the chaotic scene at Albany Airport was now more understandable.

I quickly navigated through the airport without speaking to reporters and left feeling very upset. After such a wonderful learning experience at Purdue, my week had ended on a very sad note. Once again, my guardian angel had been with me, but my thoughts were with the many who would never be coming home.

During my last couple of years in Combustion, my work mostly focused on supporting two major externally funded programs. One was a US Department of Energy (DOE) Low NOx Heavy Fuel Combustor Concept program to explore advanced combustor concepts on scaled hardware. The second was an Electric Power Research Institute (EPRI) program that essentially funded much of the prototype field test of the Multi-nozzle Quiet Combustor.

On the DOE Low NOx Heavy Fuels program, I was given a primary investigator role while working closely with Berkley Davis and a newly hired PhD, the entertaining and outspoken Dr. G. What a terrific situation for me having two highly regarded experts as co-collaborators. This was pure science, coupled with empirical experimentation—and I just loved it. From our ideas and calculations sprang forth actual miniaturized test hardware, and I was totally immersed in every step of the process.

As the program unfolded, we determined that GE's aircraft test facilities in Evendale, Ohio, more closely matched the smaller physical size of these scaled combustors, so a decision was made to sub-contract all testing to Evendale. I was designated to be the traveling liaison to personally follow each test in Ohio. Over about a six-month period, I commuted almost weekly between Schenectady and Evendale. The opportunity added to my experience base with new perspectives on design approaches along with exposure to new tools and methodologies.

Also, I experienced life in the Cincinnati suburbs of Evendale and Sharonville as I took up temporary residence at the local Marriott hotel. Adjacent to the hotel was a fine nautical-themed restaurant called Windjammer. The Windjammer had a special "captain's table" where any person dining alone could request seating and be joined by other "singles." One evening, while at the captain's table, I met a very interesting Proctor and Gamble engineer with the unusual name of King Cool. Yes, that really was his name. I just can't make this stuff up!

King was a Dutch employee of P&G who also happened to be staying at the very same hotel as me. P&G had a massive plant just up the interstate from GE's large Evendale plant where King was being trained in the latest P&G procedures. Once trained, the plan was for King to lead a new plant startup back in the Netherlands. King and I became fast friends. Over the next months, we spent a couple of weekends together in the Cincinnati area visiting local tourist spots and museums. Spontaneous encounters such as this always made my travels much more enjoyable. After concluding my assignment, I eventually lost touch with King, but I hope he did well with his big project in Holland.

I even found ways to enjoy my frequent mundane commercial commutes via the old and dingy Pittsburgh airport[53]. TWA had just initiated new commercial air service between Albany and its Pittsburgh hub, which offered the most convenient connections to Cincinnati. As a promotion to lure business travelers, TWA offered enticing First Class upgrades at a very minimal cost, subject to availability. I regularly took full advantage of that offer at my own expense, and have no regrets whatsoever. In those days, First Class travel actually included nice amenities beyond the larger leather seats. I'm talking real meals, served on linen table cloths, using real silverware and china. Oh, let's not forget free alcohol. On short flights, the attendants often provided multiple mini bottles, which I usually slipped into jacket pockets for later consumption. More than once, I forgot to remove those bottles from my person as I entered the GE plant. Remarkably, I never had any embarrassing experiences from those lapses, except for an occasional clanking of the tiny bottles.

During the Cincinnati trips, I renewed friendships with my acoustic buddy, Horst Hehmann, and some of the Callaghan LM2500 team. I enjoyed reminiscing with these folks. Thoughtfully, they arranged for me to tour the factory in my free moments. In addition to the impressive commercial engine production facility, one of the tours included an illuminating walk through a maze of underground jet engine test bunkers. My recollection is that these bunkers were built during World War II as a defense against potential bombing attacks. Yet again I was very privileged to interact with such fine, considerate professionals.

I wish I could say that the scaled low NOx testing was successful, but unfortunately it was not. While some of the concepts showed promise, and partially validated some of our theories, most resulted in major hardware

---

53 During the 1970s, the "old" Pittsburgh airport had not yet undergone the amazing transformation into one of USAir's finest and most modern hubs.

damage even before completing the test run. Adding further displeasure to disappointing test results, Dr. G and I learned that our Evendale associates secretly authored an American Society of Mechanical Engineers (ASME) technical paper on the project without informing or acknowledging either of us. Needless to say, we both were quite upset at this absolutely reprehensible and non-professional behavior.

Following a major confrontation with our management, a token acknowledgement was added at the very end of the publication. The entire episode was one of the most despicable experiences of my career. Over the years, many safeguards against such practices have been put in place both by GE and ASME. However, all these years later, the incident is still very unpleasant to recall.

Next up was the culmination of my Multi-nozzle Quiet Combustor (MNQC) project. After years of successful lab development, it was now time for the moment of truth. Field testing was to be the decisive test to determine if the MNQC would ever become a product offering. With funding secured as part of an EPRI program, a willing Southwestern utility customer stepped forward offering use of a unit located in Texas. Once again, I hit the road for an extended period. From the moment the hardware arrived, all through installation and testing, I was onsite for months personally directing the test.

In addition to the combustion system, a number of other modifications were being made to the turbine accessory systems to accommodate the MNQC. For the first time ever, we introduced use of flexible "pigtail" piping connecting fuel gas and atomizing air manifolds to each of the 10 combustors. Previously, designers and customers worried about leaks or outright failures with flexible piping on these critical combustion connections, but our accessory engineers assured us these would work. And work well they did. After our successful experience, flexible piping became standard across the product line.

The MNQC proved to be a superb success, too. While we had a few unrelated combustor setbacks, things like stuck check valves, the MNQC proved "quiet" in the field and satisfied dozens of other requirements for ignition, cross-fire, emissions and more. The customer was pleased. EPRI was pleased. GE management was pleased. The team and I were pleased. No doubt we were all very proud of working so hard on a new endeavor and bringing it to successful fruition. There is nothing like that feeling of accomplishment. The prototype MNQC hardware remained installed after our test, running for more than 8,000 fired hours of operation, without replacement, which was then a record for MS7000 units.

However, my personal euphoria was short-lived. Just days after concluding the successful test runs in Houston, I was called into my manager's office. It just happened to be a Friday afternoon, so I was expecting to hear more accolades about the MNQC test. Instead, I was about to be slammed with one of the hardest blows of my entire career.

My boss announced that I was being laid off! Really? I couldn't believe it! A whirlwind of thoughts rushed through my head. Was this somehow a delayed retaliation from my outburst about plagiarism from many months ago? Is this how GE rewards its engineers? How could this happen?

About the only answer conveyed to me was that the business was facing some difficult budget cuts, combined with the fact that I did not have an advanced degree (although I was working toward my Industrial Administration master's degree). This was not really a good explanation, but would any explanation be good enough? I headed home to ponder my future. I instantly went from playing with fire to being burned.

Here I was in May 1981, five years into my GE career, and my world was shattered. What would I do next? Was this going to be the end of what I had hoped would be a long, successful GE career? How would I recover from this? What would my colleagues think? All that I had accomplished and whatever GE career I had envisioned now appeared to be in jeopardy.

And there were no immediate answers to these troubling questions. I was experiencing the very personal trauma of a layoff. Although HR and management will tell you it's not personal, a layoff really is. I was in a really dark place that entire weekend. My GE roller coaster ride was still in its early stages, but this was undoubtedly a very low point. Little did I realize that, even in this most dismal moment, new and unexpectedly good things were about to happen.

Chapter 7

NUCLEAR DETOUR

SOMETIMES THE MOST AMAZING GIFTS are concealed in very unusual packages. My layoff turned out to be one of these unexpected gifts, but it would only be recognized as such in the clarity of hindsight years later. On Monday following my layoff notification, I showed up at my desk not knowing what to expect, but pretty sure my day wasn't going to be good. Depressed and confused, I somewhat forlornly started cleaning out my desk.

However, a light soon dawned at the end of my dark tunnel. Again, I was called into my manager's office and, as it turned out, this was a much better meeting than my last encounter. Apparently, some behind-the-scenes calls had been made on my behalf. I learned that the Gas Turbine Division was co-funding a coal gasification project at GE's Research & Development Center (RDC) in nearby Niskayuna, New York. Plans and funding were in place to test a fixed-bed coal gasifier that summer. Coincidently, RDC could use the help of a combustion engineer for the next few months—and I was instantly given a temporary assignment to work at the RDC facility while I continued to look for a permanent position.

So just that quickly, the answer to what happens next was addressed, and in a fairly positive way. Once again some "guardian angel" seemed to be looking out for me in my time of need. In any case, I certainly must give my managers credit for creating this opportunity.

After packing my belongings, I reported to RDC that very afternoon, where I was assigned a desk and phone in a mobile office. In very short order, my immediate employment uncertainty was addressed, plus I had a base from which I could pursue a new permanent position. Not bad for Day 1. Quickly, I felt a renewed optimism as this sudden turn of events helped bolster my overall attitude.

Next, I turned my attention to resume updates and hunting down job leads. Spontaneously, colleagues and friends across GE's Turbine Engineering community began reaching out, offering help and encouragement. I was really taken aback by the many people who contacted me with offers to help. Once more, I experienced another positive jolt of encouragement at a time when I needed it badly.

Two very good friends, Rich R., a fellow engineer, and his wife, Judy, who worked in Human Resources, were especially helpful. Judy sat with me, offering numerous suggestions to spiff up my resume. Rich shared valuable advice as well, no doubt some of which came from his own father, then a GE attorney. A few years later, Rich would prove instrumental in helping me land yet another important role.

Berkley Davis and Dr. G, my two PhD technical leaders from Combustion, both pledged their support and offered to provide solid technical references. Once again, I was blessed to be surrounded by such concerned co-workers who stepped up when the chips were down.

Over the next few months, while working the gasifier project, I continued to meet new and interesting people while also acquiring new skills. When learning of gasifier coal bed ignition[54] difficulties, I exercised some creativity by building a spear-like hydrogen torch igniter. Perhaps my work with hydrogen on the Callaghan, along with fuel ignition experience from Combustion, spurred my imagination. Remarkable how past experiences unknowingly prepare you for future needs.

Four solid job leads emerged over the next few months. Two were within GE and two were with "outside" companies. All had pros and cons, but in the end I suppose my desire to remain with GE won out. I focused on two GE opportunities, one with Aircraft Engines in Lynn, Massachusetts, and the other with Knolls Atomic Power Laboratory (KAPL), located next door to GE's Research Center in Niskayuna. Staying local ranked high on my priority list as I was only about 18 months from completing my graduate studies at Union College. So while the KAPL position meant shifting to a completely new environment, I zeroed in on that opportunity, even as I applied to all four positions.

KAPL, or Knolls for short, is quite a unique and, by necessity, secretive place, dedicated to supporting the US Navy nuclear propulsion program. As such, employment at the facility requires a Department of Energy security

---

54 Igniting the gasifier was akin to lighting charcoal in your backyard, only on a much larger scale.

clearance. Since the security process typically requires several months, I was even more thankful for the interim RDC position.

I knew little about nuclear reactors, so at KAPL, I would be entering an arena where much of my prior technical expertise would be of limited use. Partially offsetting that disadvantage was the fact that Knolls seemed especially interested in my previous instrumentation expertise from Measurement Services. In any case, I interviewed with an enthusiastic hiring manager I'll call JF. Instantly, I developed a comfortable rapport with him, so that was a positive omen.

Following due diligence, I also had an on-site interview at GE Aircraft Engines in Lynn. While I can't recall the name of the actual hiring manager, perhaps because he was not around during my visit there, the interview otherwise went quite well. However, what sticks in my mind about that interview was the private, one-on-one, luncheon with the group technical leader (TL). During the lunch, following a long conversation, the Lynn TL confidentially shared an important revelation: My interview had been purposefully scheduled on a day when the section level manager was out of the office. As the TL explained, this section manager was a real tyrant and had soured morale in the entire group. Two previous interviewees had turned down job offers after meeting with him.

Interestingly enough, I received offers from both KAPL and Aircraft Engines, plus one other outside firm. KAPL offered me a reasonable salary increase, but it paled in comparison to the massive offer Aircraft proposed. Now I had something to think about.

After conferring with several trusted advisors, and against some of the guidance I received, I decided to take a bit of a gamble. I contacted KAPL and explained the large disparity in offers. While I'll never know what internal communications occurred between the two GE HR groups, in the end KAPL did increase its offer. While it didn't fully match the Aircraft package, rationalized by the lower cost of living in Niskayuna vs. Boston, it was a substantial improvement over the initial offer. Without hesitation, I immediately accepted the KAPL offer. Just like that I had successfully leveraged one of my most tumultuous career experiences into the largest percentage salary increase of my entire career!

JF and the KAPL folks were most pleased with my acceptance, but I now needed that DOE security clearance. As with all KAPL offers, employment was contingent on obtaining such a clearance. Meanwhile, in the interim, I continued to work on the gasifier project. I also continued my graduate studies at Union College by taking a couple of summer courses. I had come through the trauma of a layoff and now was experiencing a very positive rebound.

After several months, my security clearance was approved and I reported to KAPL. JF and the entire KAPL team were most cordial in welcoming me. Quickly, however, I discovered that little in my prior GE experience could have prepared me for the world of KAPL. Everything in the place, particularly the offices, was quite antiquated, filled with surplus furniture in keeping with an austere culture. Hardly anything could be accomplished without excess paperwork and tedious, seemingly non-productive processes. At times it felt like I was acting in a satirical Hollywood movie. In fact, the culture, policies and procedures all directly stemmed from the conservative, uncompromising Admiral Hyman G. Rickover[55] himself. The legendary admiral's terse, often insulting mannerisms were a constant source of controversy, yet he amassed an impressive set of accomplishments, including a stellar safety record with the US Navy nuclear program. So long to the freedom and innovation of commercial GE. Welcome to GE's bureaucratic world of nuclear defense contracting.

Although KAPL was a separate division of GE in the early 1980s[56], it really bore no resemblance to any part of GE that I had experienced. My opinion is that GE kept KAPL at "arms-length," allowing the business fairly autonomous operation while benefiting from reliable, cost-plus type US government contracts. Getting adjusted to this new culture was going to be a struggle.

On the positive side, I was most fortunate to land in JF's group. I would come to appreciate JF as one of the most progressive and understanding managers at KAPL. I also found that most of the folks I encountered at KAPL were top-notch. Granted, some were a bit eccentric, but overall the people were non-pretentious and hard-working. Nowhere else in GE did I ever experience such a tight-knit worker community.

---

55 Admiral Rickover, who originally led development of the US Naval Nuclear Program, was often referred to as the "Father of the Nuclear Navy." The admiral created his share of controversy associated with his blunt, sometimes insulting and always demanding manners.

56 Under Chairman Jack Welch, GE would later sell KAPL to Bechtel. It now is operated by Lockheed Martin.

Most of JF's team, numbering six or seven of us, were co-located in what was called a "secure" area, meaning we had an additional badge-activated security door limiting access to our office area. In fact, it was a welcome relief to work in this area as I was already struggling to adapt to so many new procedures. I didn't need the added burden of locking daily work in safes each night. Security violations at KAPL were taken very seriously, and offenses could result in significant penalties, including dismissal.

Happily for me, some very interesting characters shared this office area, and I can't possibly imagine getting through my days working at KAPL without them. Two who ultimately became my closest friends: Joe Shatas and John "JD" Warren[57]. My connection with Joe and JD also opened the door to meeting a host of additional KAPL "characters."

Joe and JD kept me "grounded" as I became assimilated into KAPL and struggled with its bureaucracy. Both were a continual source of amusement that provided a welcome diversion from the autocratic environment. Like almost everyone else at KAPL, they were both technically very sharp and could explain any technical questions I had. Beyond that, I could especially count on them to keep me straight regarding the many new and unusual practices followed in the lab. To reciprocate, I shared "real-world" stories from my experiences in the commercial side of GE. The stories represented a kind of alternative universe that they only imagined existed, as they had both joined KAPL directly from college.

At times, I became totally exasperated trying to comply with KAPL procedures. JF, my leader, was blessed with abundant patience. This became quite evident to me following an early misadventure that since evolved into a classic humorous episode that the gang never let me forget.

One St. Patrick's Day, Joe convinced me to ride with him to a popular downtown Schenectady pub called the Electric Grinch. Initially, I was a bit hesitant, but given the holiday and Joe's persuasiveness, I agreed to go. After over an hour of food and libations, with a work deadline hanging over my head, I suggested we return to the office. Instead, my fun-loving friend decided to take a free shuttle to continue to celebrate at the Grinch's sister pub in downtown Albany. I would have to return to KAPL in a cab.

---

57 I started calling him JD after learning his middle initial. It seemed to just stick, and soon most folks picked up on it.

Now Schenectady never was known as a good "taxi" city. After multiple calls, I finally contacted a company that promised a cab would be dispatched "shortly." Meanwhile, using the only available public payphone (no cell phones in those days), I tried to contact the office to let folks know I would be returning late. But the combination of loud background music and the boisterous crowd made communication via phone all but impossible. Back at the office, my call apparently sounded like a prank, and I was twice disconnected.

When I finally got back to my desk at about 3 p.m., JF was sitting there completing the paperwork I was supposed to finish. Not good. I tried to explain my absence, but as soon as I mentioned Joe's name, JF raised his hand, an understanding smirk crossing his face. No further explanation was necessary, he said. I couldn't believe it. Anywhere else in commercial GE I'm sure there would have been unpleasant repercussions, but JF simply wrote that one off. Thank you again, JF!

JF's small team actually was providing technical support to a much larger project within KAPL known as the Advanced Reactor Project (ARP). As I learned, KAPL was in competition with a sister lab known as Bettis, run by GE rival Westinghouse, for the next new naval propulsion reactor project. Such large complex projects spanned several years, and the awarding of ARP was many months, if not years, away. While I certainly appreciated and understood the need for long-range planning, I struggled with the level of detail I was being asked to develop at such an early stage. From prior commercial practice, I recognized the reality that any such detailed plans change constantly, so I viewed the effort as a "make work" assignment. JF and I seemed to clash regularly over these "bubble" chart plans. God bless JF for his tolerance!

Perhaps to appease my dislike of the bubble charts, JF leveraged my knowledge of advanced measurement equipment by assigning me to lead a large capital equipment procurement effort. I gladly accepted the undertaking, thankful to get some temporary relief from the bubble plans. Immediately, I was encouraged to see that the approved vendor list included Hewlett Packard, which I still considered to be the premier provider of the most user-friendly specialized measurement electronics available. I looked forward to catching up on the latest innovations now being offered.

My early enthusiasm quickly evaporated, however, as I bumped up against entrenched KAPL red tape. Capital equipment purchases in the defense contractor world require exhaustive explanations on endless forms, all of which required multiple levels of approval. I exercised all of my resourcefulness in trying to convince non-technical paper pushers about the unique functionality and benefits that HP offered, since they were not the preferred low-cost supplier.

One unique innovation from HP was a direct interface with, what was then, one of the most advanced desktop computers available. Said computer could be used to integrate, control, calibrate and analyze a variety of measurements, streamlining the entire testing process and providing a complete package of hardware, software and analytics. In commercial GE, such a purchase likely would have been executed in a month or two, but at KAPL, with its endless chain of reviews, approvals and signoffs, the process dragged on for the better part of a year. Eventually, my persistence paid off, and I obtained the necessary approvals and ordered the HP equipment.

When the electronics finally arrived on site, it was like Christmas morning as giant boxes were delivered to our secure office area. I was given a new work space designated for checkout and familiarization with our new "toys". JD, who worked in an adjacent cubicle, simply could not resist the temptation to immerse himself, experimenting on the powerful new HP desktop computer. Throughout his entire career, JD was a software, computer and simulation expert. Part of each workday he was right alongside me as we tested the new equipment.

To better set the stage here, the 1980s represented the dawn of what would become a megatrend in personal computing as new more powerful chips became available. A groundbreaking new California technology company called Apple had thrust itself onto the scene by introducing a new wave of desktop, easy-to-use personal computers. Floppy disks, those flexible 5.25-inch squares, encasing thin, round magnetically sensitive surfaces, were the rage for storing and transferring data.

HP was quick to pounce on the rapidly growing computer technology, designing its own more powerful laptops to interface with its front-running electronic measurement devices. Operating with an enhanced BASIC programming language, the HP laptop I purchased for KAPL was one of the most cutting-edge available. Ironically, I also was using a very similar, user-friendly BASIC language on an Apple PC as part of my graduate studies at

Union College. Yet again, this is another example of a remarkable coincidence that nicely connected seemingly unrelated prior experiences into an unexpected common purpose.

Much to my amazement, I soon discovered a "Star Trek©"[58] game had been included with the HP computer, ostensibly as a demonstration of the PC's capabilities. Since both JD and I were huge sci-fi fans, we could hardly believe our good fortune. Lunch time, or basically any spare moment, became game time, as we fought off Klingon attacks with phasors and photon torpedoes. Although we disabled the sound effects to avoid disrupting the entire office, our periodic yelps of frustration at unintended outcomes betrayed our game playing. Had the KAPL "PC police" ever discovered this demo, I'm sure we would have been forced to remove it, but that didn't happen. Meanwhile most of the prior generation employees were appalled by our antics and thought we were completely insane.

Yet the "Star Trek" demo game was not the end of our PC capers. While experimenting with the internal random number function, another thought crossed my mind. A Union professor had often used gambling analogies to demonstrate certain statistical concepts. With that in mind, JD and I decided a much more entertaining approach to testing PC randomization capabilities would be programing it to play craps. It was a great exercise that proved quite addictive. Over lunch, we left the PC running 50,000 simulated dice rolls as we tested various strategies. After all, in the real world we wanted to be reasonably sure about expected outcomes before risking our money at a casino!

Ultimately, the HP equipment was checked out, and we were able to demonstrate its actual engineering capabilities. At this point our group had no immediate need for the equipment, so another group took over usage for an upcoming component test. I hope that somewhere out in the oceans of the world, there are US nuclear subs and carriers benefiting from improvements developed and validated using the HP equipment I helped to procure.

While the HP computer and associated equipment presented an amusing diversion, I soon came to the realization that I really liked and missed working on gas turbines. Marching through the daily KAPL routines was not cutting it. I was not now, nor would I likely ever become, captivated by nuclear re-

---

58 Reference the original sci-fi TV series created by Gene Roddenberry from the late 1960s.

actors. Working in the very restrictive KAPL environment, where individual creativity was shunned, simply was not in my nature. My passion was for gas turbines, and that's where I longed to be. At this point, I challenged myself to find a new job, ideally with GE's Gas Turbine division, but definitely somewhere that would give me the autonomy I thrived on. My advice to anyone in this situation is to follow your internal guidance and move on to something you are passionate about. To really be successful, you'll need to be passionate about your work. Do not stagnate in a place you are not happy.

Despite my work frustrations, I continued to enjoy the camaraderie with my new-found KAPL associates. Friday nights meant parties or happy hours often followed by terrific dinners. Holidays, birthdays, weddings or other events provided further incentives for gatherings. Halloweens never were more fun as we attended elaborate costume parties that sometimes spilled over to local establishments. A more congenial group I have never encountered. Clearly, my colleagues also struggled in the KAPL environment, leading to a continual atmosphere of merriment outside of work.

While at KAPL I continued to pursue my graduate studies in Business and Industrial Administration at Union College, fully utilizing GE's wonderful tuition refund program. Some of my KAPL co-workers also were enrolled in the same graduate program, so we sometimes partnered together on group assignments, which I thoroughly enjoyed.

In June 1983, after five years of part-time evening and summer classes, I graduated from Union College with a Master of Science degree in Industrial Administration. My parents, along with my Aunt Gina and Uncle Henry, who had encouraged me to complete the master program, all attended my graduation ceremony on a hot June day. A number of my KAPL associates, including JD and Joe, attended my graduation party as well.

There is no doubt in my mind, that GE's tuition refund program was one of the best benefits I ever utilized. Earning that degree was a milestone personal accomplishment, but little did I realize what a big factor my newly earned degree would play in the continuation of my GE career.

While at KAPL, I wisely had maintained contact with many of my Gas Turbine colleagues. Sometimes interactions were formal, as in luncheon events or calls, but some were less formally, such as participating in sports and other social activities. I especially enjoyed our Gas Turbine summer softball league, so I continued playing on the team even while at KAPL. We named our softball team the "Survivors," in testament to our fortitude to stay employed despite the relentless layoffs under GE Chairman Jack Welch. Looking back at a team photo, it's incredible that virtually everyone on that team, including me, ultimately became a GE manager at one point in his career. Quite a team! But I'm getting ahead of myself.

Contact with my former colleagues payed off big one day when my good buddy Rich R. gave me a heads up about a position in Gas Turbine Application Engineering. In fact, the position was his, but he would soon be promoted to a new role in Sales. Rich knew how badly I wanted to return to Gas Turbine, and he thought I would be a good fit in the role. At the time, I didn't fully appreciate or comprehend what the Application role was all about, but I started digging into it. In short order, I sent a hard copy resume in parallel with officially posting via GE's internal hiring system.

In the posting I noticed two key requirements for the position. One was at least five years' prior experience in gas turbine design and the second was a Master of Science degree. It was absolutely unbelievable that only six months earlier I had completed my MS degree at Union College. In another amazing coincidence, I had almost exactly five years' experience in Combustion, which qualified me on both counts. Talk about fate and circumstance intervening once again!

In short order, I completed the paperwork, and the waiting game began. Weeks passed and, with the suspense killing me, I finally made a call to the hiring manager, Bob Gessner. It was great to learn that Bob was about to contact me to schedule a personal interview. As we were both motivated, we set a date and time right then and there. Soon, I was sitting in Bob's office reviewing my GE background. My five years of gas turbine combustion experience was clearly of most interest to Bob. After that interview, I met with Bob's immediate manager, who I'll refer to as RA, and perhaps with one or two others. As I left, I felt very positive about the job and the interview. No doubt this job would stretch me into areas where I had very little background, but with the confidence amassed in my career thus far, I was sure I could learn quickly and adapt to situations as needed.

Once again, weeks passed, and I heard absolutely nothing. Finally, I contacted Bob and asked about the situation. Bob was most surprised by my call and stated that he had sent me an offer via KAPL HR and was awaiting my response! What? I told Bob I would work the situation from my end and get back to him promptly.

Arriving at the KAPL HR office, I asked for the person handling my paperwork and discovered the person was out. The "cover person" did, however, locate what turned out to be my "offer letter" stashed in a pile. At this point I finally had physical custody of Bob's offer, my ticket out of KAPL. That evening I wrote my acceptance and the next day, I hand delivered it to Bob, apologizing for the KAPL snafu.

As I would learn later, KAPL had ways of disrupting "outside" offers, even from other GE departments. The vetting process of government clearance was a long and expensive one, and there was an aversion to letting cleared folks walk out the door. KAPL often tried to dissuade folks from leaving. In my case, KAPL even offered to match the Gas Turbine salary increase. Of course, as I explained, this transfer really wasn't about money. With the stage now set for my return to the Gas Turbine business, I was anxious to plow ahead. My future was calling, and many more amazing adventures were about to unfold.

Chapter 8

WHERE HAVE I LANDED?

AFTER A THREE-YEAR HIATUS, I had finally returned to the Gas Turbine business, but this new role felt quite different from my prior stint in Combustion. For starters, I was in a new office location at a former Army Depot, miles away from the main downtown Schenectady plant where my career began. Most associates here were completely new to me. I also felt a bit overwhelmed by my new position as an Application Engineer. Instead of focusing on one major subsystem, as I was when working in Combustion, now I was responsible for the entire gas turbine and the generator, plus a host of accessory equipment we sometimes referred to as "balance of plant," or BOP. Expanding my knowledge universe to match this wider area of responsibility was not going to be easy.

To paint the picture a bit more clearly, let me try to convey what Application Engineering means, at least in the GE context as I experienced it. In a nutshell, Applications Engineering provided technical support to Sales and Marketing for GE's Power Generation business. For each new project, Application Engineers (AEs) normally began by reading customer Requests for Proposal (RFP), which usually contained a very detailed technical equipment specification from the customer. RFPs could range from five or six page documents up through multiple volumes containing thousands of pages. Flowing from interpretation of the RFP, AE's were expected to provide seven essential deliverables:

1. A scope of supply and internal configuration document we called PEGASUS
2. Technical comments, clarifications or exceptions to the RFP
3. Technical guarantees for performance, emissions, acoustics or other guarantees, plus any required Equipment Data Sheets
4. Manufacturing commitment on equipment deliverable dates
5. Engineering commitment on project-specific drawing deliverable dates

6. Cost and cycle estimates for non-standard options

7. A proposal mechanical outline and electrical one-line drawing

Touching all seven of the above "bases" typically involved communication with a small army of internal GE personnel across the US and sometimes abroad. The number of supporting cast members varied significantly depending on many factors, including the RFP size and complexity along with the AEs' experience level[59]. Beyond just reading through the RFP, the most difficult and time consuming were Nos. 2, 3 and 6. Examples and better understanding of the difficulties will become apparent as I cover some real-world situations in this and the following chapters.

Probably the best account I can give describing my first months in Applications would be the proverbial "drinking from a fire hose" analogy. People, information, and procedures were flying at me at an incredible pace. The intensity was driven by a number of factors, including equipment/bid complexity, relatively short bidding cycles, sheer number of bids relative to the number of engineers, and even our own cumbersome, internal processes. In addition, a typical AE would be working on three to five new bids at any given time. In peak periods, that number could double, creating almost unimaginable conflict and stress on everyone. Interruptions, such as travel for follow-up meetings or questions responding to previously submitted bids, only further complicated the situation, leading to numerous priority skirmishes.

Over my first weeks and months, I spent countless hours reviewing publications, studying equipment drawings, and meeting some of the supporting experts to gather information. Essentially, I was struggling to create a library of hard copy resources, along with a network of internal GE expertise necessary to satisfy the aforementioned deliverables. While in hindsight it's relatively easy to summarize the situation, back then I didn't have the experience or conceptual visualization to see my job that clearly.

Applications put me on the steepest learning curve I have ever encountered. The volume of information needed to execute each job was incredible, so the learning curve sustained itself at a very high level for months—and even years—on end. While I worked countless casual overtime hours playing catch-up, the fact of the matter was that, even if it were possible to work 24 hours a

---

59 Inexperienced AEs would need to make many more contacts

day, it would not have been enough. Over time, the learning curve only negligibly decreased in slope, but it never flattened. In reality, it would take several years to simply attain a passable level of competence. GE's dynamic products, complex markets and demanding customers continually pushed the envelope, requiring a constant refresh of our knowledge and skill sets.

A treasure trove of technical information was imbedded in two basic proposal drawings, the mechanical outline and electrical one-line (Item 7 above). Ideally, AEs were to create proposal-specific versions of these two drawings[60], which used a specialized language of symbols, diagrams and otherwise abbreviated nomenclature to convey this information. Back in my Combustion days, I never even knew these drawings existed, as my world focused on a single subsystem.

On the surface, the mechanical outline didn't seem that intimidating. Mainly focusing on the turbine generator layout, it contained key dimensions of the centerline equipment. Additional pages included further detailed information on accessory skids, interfaces, and equipment footprints. Our customers almost always focused on the accessories, such as inlet filtration and ducting, exhausts and other free-standing modules. In fact, we had the greatest flexibility with accessories, so discussions around these components always seemed to generate the longest, most contentious debates. Since I was a mechanical engineer by training, I more easily handled the mechanical discussions. However, given so many detailed nuances with every component, I was always hard-pressed trying to juggle the numerous, sometimes inconsistent, specific customer requirements in their specifications. Without exaggeration, I can say I learned something new about our equipment at every customer meeting.

Then there is the electrical one-line diagram[61]. Here, I really struggled, as I was not technically strong in this area. Looking at the one-line drawing sheets was akin to reading Egyptian hieroglyphics from the walls of the great pyramid. Slowly, painfully, after months talking with many of our electrical

---

60 Given short proposal cycle times, and lower priority for proposal drawings, often there was not time for drafting to create specific proposal versions, so standard default drawings were often used instead.

61 This is a high-level electrical diagram showing electrical connections, protection, breakers, switches, transformers, etc. for the entire turbine generator package right up to the station step up transformer. Other pages described an auxiliary transformer to feed lower voltage power to package accessories.

experts, and perhaps even through a bit of osmosis, I got to the point where I could at least be one or two questions deep on this data-packed drawing. Unfortunately, many of our customers wanted to delve five or six questions deep.

A wealth of information could be summarized on the mechanical outline and electrical one-line drawings. The trick was to master the nomenclature, symbols and other short-hand notations to unlock the hidden data. Gradually, I began to assimilate this knowledge, but it literally took me years to fully appreciate and become proficient at it.

Going just one step further was another set of drawings known as schematics. In total there were perhaps 20 of these, although not every system would be included on every turbine-generator package. They included the lube oil system, fire protection, cooling water, liquid and gas fuel systems, ventilation, and water wash. Schematics again heavily utilized even more specialized symbols indicating valves, sensors, gauges and switches as they traced critical flow paths for liquids or gases. A kind of master decoder document, known as the Device Summary, helped interpret many different symbols used on the schematics. In aggregate, these primary drawings represented a mere fraction of the information I would regularly draw upon, but they were a good grounding point upon which to build. Over time, I started collecting "go folders" that contained the standard set of these basic drawings for each of our products. These folders were a handy resource for the many times I was pulled into impromptu meetings or phone calls—or even sent on trips—with little or no prior notice. It sure helped to be able to grab these documents, which put a wealth of information at my fingertips[62].

Without the luxury of formal training, most of my learning occurred on the job during the pressure-packed proposal preparation process. In the worst cases, learning would occur in a face-to-face customer meeting. Demonstrating ignorance in such an open forum is never a good idea—and sometimes is career limiting—but it would happen on occasion.

In customer meetings, I was constantly asked questions for which I didn't know the answer. Over time I became more adept at handling these inquiries and even learned to sense when I was being "baited." For example, I might reflect the inquiry back, asking what the customer really wanted to know. Often

---

62 Unfortunately, the internet and personal laptop computer use at GE were still nearly a decade away!

this would open an entirely new area of discussion, perhaps in a somewhat different subject area from the original question. Sometimes it would even lead me to an answer I could provide. In the end, if I just couldn't provide an answer, I simply admitted so, but promised to follow up, which I always did. Stories abound about those who tried to "make up" answers. Almost always, such situations ended badly, often destroying the speakers' credibility and sometimes GE's as well. I never ventured down the road of make believe.

Technical skills were only part of Application Engineering. For instance, I had daily contact with dozens of people within the GE network, spread across America and in many cases around the entire globe. GE power plant equipment was produced in multiple locations, much in the US, but our Sourcing people searched globally for competitive suppliers. Obtaining and processing information from this vast network was a monumental challenge. People skills, which I seemed to have a knack for, were especially useful here.

The subject areas of contracts and commercial risks also were new to me. These risks included contractual clauses with defined penalties for things like performance deficiencies, non-compliance with air emissions, equipment noise levels, and a host of other equipment-related parameters. Additionally, schedules for drawings, equipment delivery, testing and commercial operation dates also were contractual obligations subject to financial penalties. These high-stakes face-to-face meetings and negotiations with customers were a new, demanding experience, too. Surprisingly, despite the stressful nature of such meetings, I came to enjoy them.

Everything I was experiencing in Applications was happening against a backdrop of business dynamics, creating its own set of significant distractions. CEO Jack Welch had moved into the GE chairman role roughly about the same time I joined KAPL. In the isolated world of KAPL, such a change really had minimal, if any, impact. But here in the commercial world of a flagship GE business, things were really starting to rock. By moving back to commercial GE, I had inadvertently placed myself directly in the crosshairs where I would experience first-hand decades of upheaval Welch brought upon the business.

During the early 1980s, Welch made his presence felt in his unrelenting drive to maximize profits at any cost. GE's Schenectady employment levels suffered roughly a 50% reduction between 1981 and 1990 under Welch's leadership. Over the next five years, the Schenectady workforce would be halved yet again. Welch had no tolerance for business cycles, as he always appeared to be myopically fixated on improving successive quarterly results. From my vantage point, the Power business seemed to lack a long-term corporate perspective, backed by investments and commitment through all business cycles. Decisions to forego or minimize long-term investments, such as R&D or new product development, would end up costing the Power business dearly for decades.

Welch's management style of instilling conflict and fear[63] caused havoc throughout the Schenectady plant, creating adversarial relationships with the union and the city of Schenectady itself. Welch seemed to be conducting a personal vendetta against the Schenectady plant, particularly against the labor union, which represented thousands of hourly workers. Constant tax assessment battles raged annually with the city as GE demolished obsolete, unused buildings in the plant. This most definitely was not a pleasant backdrop for inspiring people to give their all.

Technological change was happening at an ever faster pace as well. An entire new megatrend that would become known as digitization was occurring, driven by ever smaller, faster and less expensive computer chips. Office productivity was set to soar as new, more powerful desktop computers and word processors were gradually moving into everyday use. This was only the initial wave of momentous technological shifts that impacted my entire work experience. Still bigger changes were yet to come with the internet, email and cell phones, but they were still years down the road.

During the 1980s, Power Generation Sales was basically a very centrally controlled operation at GE. That is, Sales, Marketing and Proposal activities were handled in Schenectady headquarters. Global sales offices, in various regions, were the tentacles for gathering information[64], which then was communicated back to HQ. Strategic business decisions, proposal creation and all follow-on sales activities were handled by Schenectady HQ. So it was

---

63 This is my personal reflection on how Welch constantly set virtually unreachable, conflicting goals, with the constant threat of selling a business or firing leaders who failed to meet those goals.

64 Local Sales folks were responsible for thoroughly knowing their particular customers. As the local "face" of GE, it was necessary for them to understand customer needs, finances, competitive landscape, key decision makers and any other strategic business information pertinent to GE equipment needs.

here, in Schenectady, at the receiving end of all this input, my Applications team was co-located with Sales and Marketing.

Most of the regional sales folks were indispensable when it came to on-site meetings, particularly bid negotiations. Customer visits generally were led by a salesperson from headquarters. Sometimes only an application engineer and salesperson, along with the local field representative, comprised the entire team. On larger more complex projects, the team would expand to include whatever additional functions (legal, projects, finance, specialized technical experts, etc.) were necessary. Whenever the headquarters team arrived, we had almost a celebrity status with the locals. It really was an honor and privilege to be a part of these teams.

The local GE contacts typically provided excellent briefings prior to our customer meetings. Often, these briefings and strategy reviews occurred over superb meals at fine establishments. The local GE folks always made me feel at home, no matter where in the world I traveled. Although GE covered our travel and living expenses, it was customary for the local salesperson to arrange for and pay for most meals during our visit.

Local folks understood inside details on each customer, who the key decision makers were, where the hard points were in our bid and the like. On the downside, most did not have a deep technical understanding about our products. Also, because the local team needed to maintain a positive and regular relationship with customers, they were not the ones to cover onerous points. That challenging job was reserved for our headquarters team. If such issues were technical in nature, then the responsibility fell squarely on the AE. Welcome to the big leagues!

Up to this point in my career, I had never held a job that directly mattered so much to our business. As the key technical lead for onsite meetings and negotiations, the AE had a huge influence on a project. Recognizing the importance of the AE, screening for these positions was rigorous. No one was hired into an Applications role without prior experience elsewhere within GE and preferably direct experience on gas, steam or generator products. My five years of Combustion experience helped me meet this stringent screening criteria. Knowledge of air emissions was a critical skill that helped differentiate me from my co-workers, each of whom had their own differentiating skill sets. Expanding my expertise gave me great leverage for some impactful experiences. Not only was my background experience crucial in being hired, but it would be a major influence that propelled me on a continued growth path.

At customer meetings, AEs were always expected assume the technical lead on technical issues. At the very top of the list is performance, or basically how much electricity could be generated and how much fuel was needed to make that electricity. Another important topic was exhaust air emissions. Most parts of the industrialized world carefully regulate equipment that produces emissions. Air emission discussions played directly into my background. Having a strong chemistry aptitude, plus my Combustion experience, also helped me absorb a significant amount of new expertise needed in the role. The ever-changing regulatory landscapes kept me constantly attuned to new developments in this area.

Clean air was a personal passion for me, so I took this part of my job very seriously. We only have this planet, and we've already done plenty of harm to it. At GE, we had a good story to tell. I had a solid understanding of the benefits of GE technology so I was determined to deliver a clear and compelling message to our customers.

Complicating everything was the fact that many customers engaged the help of Architectural/Engineering (sometimes called A/E[65]) firms to handle the entire bidding process, and in my personal experience, GE was often in an adversarial position with them. The relationship was not totally unlike dealing with a purchasing or real estate agent. The agent, in this case the A/E firm, has primary loyalty to those writing the checks. Therefore, A/E's strived to prove their value to the end customer, which often translated into squeezing "deep pockets" GE for every possible advantage. Sometimes, the A/E firms would develop their own equipment specification that was either customized with, or simply supplied in addition to, a customer RFP. It was not completely unheard of for multiple specifications to actually be in direct conflict. Meetings often got quite contentious, perhaps driven by embarrassment, when these contradictions were pointed out.

Yes, when I joined Applications, I entered a very competitive battlefield that moved at incredible speed. Heaven help you if you didn't keep up. It's

---

65 I'll use the A/E nomenclature to avoid confusion with my AE (no slash) abbreviation for Applications Engineer.

hard to believe that I not only "adjusted" to this maddening pace, but somehow came to enjoy, and even thrive, in it. Yet, the more I learned the more I found I needed to learn. It was a never-ending cycle involving dynamic, complex products and demanding customers whose needs were always evolving. Our products evolved also, to address those changing customer needs. Each project came with its own unique set of circumstances reflecting a particular combination of customer demands, timetables and always high expectations.

As I quickly discovered, product line engineering folks really didn't have time to help AEs. Pressures and metrics tied to existing requisition deadlines were their primary concern, so in our proposal efforts, we were just irritants in their daily routine. As a result, some were helpful and others provided incomplete or downright incorrect information just to be rid of us. I had to quickly determine who was giving good solid responses and who was just blowing smoke.

As I would come to learn, Applications was a strange twilight area between Sales/Marketing and Engineering. Although Applications was technically part of Engineering, we never were quite recognized as such by the broader engineering community. Instead, we were often treated as unwanted step-children, since Applications had no design ownership on any specific component. On the other hand, Sales/Marketing leaned on us heavily to address complex technical concerns from customers, yet always kept us at arms-length as we certainly were not part of Sales' commercial world. While I sensed this situation, I tried not to concern myself with this "step-child" syndrome, but I did recognize the issues it created. Instead, I focused on playing a critical role to help win orders for our equipment.

After only a few months on the job, which somehow seemed much longer, I was sent on my first trip to support negotiations with our Sales team. Now I would have thought this first project would involve a short domestic journey without many complications, so I could just get my feet wet. No such thing! My first trip as an AE took me almost as far from my home base in Schenectady as you could possibly go on the globe—Singapore. So many firsts—my first Asia trip, my first trans-Pacific trip, the farthest I'd ever traveled etc. Most important, this was my first face-to-face negotiation with a difficult customer.

Almost everything about this long trans-Pacific trip was eye popping for me. At the time, GE permitted international travelers to fly business class, which made the nearly 24-plus hour trip much more comfortable. On this trip, I flew my first 747SP[66] for the first leg of the journey, a grueling 14-hour non-stop flight from JFK to Tokyo's Narita airport. On this very unique flight, we departed Kennedy around noon and literally "chased the sun" westward, experiencing probably the longest period of uninterrupted daylight on the planet. During the JFK-to-Tokyo leg, I traveled with a team of perhaps three colleagues. The more experienced travelers suggested we do an extended layover in Tokyo to rest up prior to continuing on the final leg to Singapore. I did a somewhat shorter layover than the others, perhaps about 20 hours, before resuming my journey. In Tokyo, we stayed at the famous Okura Hotel where dignitaries often stay during visits to the Japanese capital. The Okura is located near the US Embassy in Tokyo, so I briefly visited there during the stopover. International travel had some nice perks, despite the sometimes-debilitating jet lag.

When I landed at Singapore's spacious, modern and visually impressive Changi Airport, I was taken aback. It seems the airport itself could have been my destination. Never before or since have I seen such a beautiful airport on such an enormous scale. Shops of every variety, dining to please any taste, exotic plants, trees and even a waterfall, encompassed me as I walked toward customs. The place was palatial with carpets, lighting and eye-catching delights almost anywhere you looked. Whatever my preconceived idea of Asia being a third world region may have been, Changi airport instantly dispelled that false impression.

Within minutes of our arrival, at least six other 747s had also landed, yet I did not experience any customs delay whatsoever—a tribute to a well-designed and efficient airport at a major Asian crossroad. I really didn't want to leave the airport, but after traveling for so many long hours over two days, I was looking forward to a good meal and some rest. Reluctantly, I changed some money and caught a cab to my downtown hotel.

Upon arriving at the luxurious Shangri La Hotel, for the second time in my brief visit, I was taken aback by the splendid and lavish beauty of the impressive surroundings. Almost immediately I felt welcomed and comfortable in this exotic new country so very far from home. Like my airport arrival, my hotel check-in was quick and efficient. A welcome message from

---

66 SP stood for Special Performance, an enhanced version of the iconic jet. PanAm World Airways had recently introduced the new plane, which was the longest range aircraft in commercial service and the first to fly non-stop between New York and Tokyo.

our local GE host was awaiting me at check-in informing me of an upcoming poolside strategy meeting with the team the following day (which was a Sunday). Nice touch to meet at the pool! Kudos to our Salesman.

Joining me on this trip was a great guy named Darwin Brudos, who managed one of GE's Gas Turbine Controls groups. It was both a comfort and a bit of a relief to have such a valuable electrical expert with me. He and I were the technical experts who would address question after question from a very contentious customer. And bombarded we were! From early morning until early evening each day we were pelted with very detailed questions about our equipment and pressed to complete dozens of "fill in" equipment data sheets[67] from among the hundreds of pages the customer had requested. Often this information was not especially relevant to our equipment, yet the customer insisted they be completed. Darwin and I spent hours sorting these out. Still other information simply was beyond our combined knowledge, so each day we made a list of "open" questions and each evening, taking advantage of the 12 hour time shift, I faxed this information back to my office. While we slept, the time change allowed Bob Gessner and our colleagues back in Schenectady to track down the requested information. The next morning, I would stop in the Shangri La business office to pick up replies. This routine continued for an entire week. Nothing like round-the-clock efforts to win an order.

After more than a week in Singapore, our negotiations wound down and it was time to head home. I had no idea how well we had done, so it fell to our local Sales contacts to keep us informed. As we would learn later, our GE bid was merely a "check bid" on this project. At the time, GE had never won a major power generation project in Singapore, and it would be no different this time. The hours of detailed questions were simply to fulfil the customer obligation to validate comparison with other manufacturers. Our responses, or lack thereof, provided grounds upon which to reject our proposal and award the project to a long-time, well entrenched, competitor. Occasionally, I worked on other such "check" or "wired" bids where the winning bidder was essentially pre-determined long before the actual award was made. In times like these, working so hard and so long supporting GE bid efforts could be frustrating and discouraging. Yet, as I would learn, it was all part of the job.

---

67 Customers would often include fill-in-the-blank detailed data sheets asking for minute details of each piece of equipment GE supplied, even if that equipment was not applicable to our bid.

Due to our extended meetings, my original flight plans were scrapped, so I rebooked my travel itinerary. To my surprise, there were no available seats for the next couple of days, except in First Class, for the initial outbound segments. A GE executive on the trip, facing the same dilemma, advised me to do the upgrade as opposed to extending hotel and living expenses, which were deemed even more costly than the fare difference. Happily, I complied.

My new booking on Singapore Airlines, one of the world's finest carriers, routed me via Hong Kong with a continuing leg on to Honolulu, Hawaii. I decided because of the upcoming Memorial Day holiday that I would spend the weekend exploring Hawaii at my own expense, as I had never been there before. Extended layovers, especially in exotic locales, would become a trademark of my business travels. It's something I never ever regretted, and I would highly recommend to anyone. Take a few minutes to "smell the roses" and enjoy spontaneous opportunity when you get the chance.

Without question that Singapore Airlines 747 trip back to Hawaii via Hong Kong ranked as one of the most magnificent flights I ever took. Sitting only two rows behind me in First Class was actress Connie Stevens, who had been performing in Singapore. I had a very brief yet cordial exchange with her during the flight. Traveling First Class really had some nice perks, and I loved every minute of it.

During the stopover in Hong Kong, I walked up the 747s distinctive spiral staircase and poked my head in the open flight deck door. I presented my GE business card, mentioned I was a Cessna pilot and asked if I might briefly visit the cockpit. To my surprise, an American captain was carefully overseeing two very young Singapore nationals, one in the co-pilot seat and the other at the flight engineer station. After briefly scanning my business card, the Captain explained things were quite busy prepping for our overnight flight to Hawaii. Nevertheless, he nonchalantly suggested I stop back up to the flight deck once we reached cruising altitude. Instantly, my mind flashed back to another captain, years earlier, who had invited me to ride in the jump seat of a GE corporate jet. Thanking the Captain, I hastily retreated to my seat, but I was sky high long before our aircraft ever left the ground.

Naturally, I took the Captain up on his offer. For the first time ever, I was welcomed onto a commercial 747 flight deck with the aircraft in flight! On the darkened flight deck, only the dim glow of instruments provided minimal illumination, allowing the pilots to maintain their night vision. I was simply awe-struck. There was the captain, completely relaxed with his feet up on top of his forward panel as he beckoned me to a seat directly behind his[68]. With the aircraft on autopilot, the aforementioned two young flight crew members were carefully monitoring their respective aircraft instruments, under the watchful eye of the experienced captain. As hundreds of unsuspecting passengers slept quietly in their seats, here I was having a spectacular cockpit tour of a 747 in flight!

Sensing my awe, the captain began briefly reviewing flight instruments that precisely pinpointed our current course, altitude, speed and location. Realizing I was a gas turbine engineer, he also discussed engine performance as he pointed out those gauges to me. Surprisingly, he was even briefly apologetic as he noted that, despite his recommendation for GE engines, the airline had chosen a com-petitor engine for its 747 fleet. Before I left the flight deck, the captain demon-strated his latest onboard color weather radar. At the time, we were about to pass over Taiwan, which could actually be seen on radar. To validate the radar screen, the captain had me stand to get a forward view out the cockpit window. As I peered into the inky night blackness, I observed lights on the island nation nearly seven miles below. In all my years of commercial travel around the globe, this was one of the best flights I ever had, on a world-class airline with an extraor-dinary crew. I can't imagine how anyone could be any more fortunate.

From a business standpoint, the Singapore project encapsulated what the Applications job was all about. The project exposed me to the full proposal cycle, except for winning the order. But I would get many more opportunities on that front. I had only completed the first of what would eventually become hundreds of such experiences.

Ultimately, my position in Application Engineering would become career defining. The journey spanned extraordinary people, places and situations. Global-scale sales of high-value capital equipment like power plants is truly a complex endeavor. So many new experiences, challenges and situations required me to leverage the sum of my prior knowledge and draw on inner strengths I didn't even realize I had.

---

68 On larger long-range aircraft, flight decks sometimes have additional seating for an extra pilot. Such was the case here.

Chapter 9

HARPOONING A WHALE

RETURNING FROM THE GRUELING, NEARLY 20,000-mile Singapore trip—including stopovers in Tokyo, Hong Kong and Hawaii—somehow I felt energized. Despite minimal negotiating experience, the distant meeting locale, and a contentious, demanding customer, I had survived my initial customer meeting and was now baptized into the world of high-value capital equipment sales. And, I discovered, I had actually enjoyed the experience.

GE has always been a very dynamic place, and as I continued to progress in my Applications role in the later 1980s, many changes were continuing to take shape. The Applications team grew into three subgroups: Utility, Industrial and After-market, with personnel changes in all three. One of the new additions was a former controls engineer named Frank Brooks. Personally, I was especially glad an experienced Controls/Electrical expert had joined the group. The controls and electrical subject areas admittedly were my Achilles heel, so I appreciated having an in-house "expert" for advice.

While I can't say exactly what it is that makes two individuals particularly compatible, Frank and I had it. We bonded immediately, and the magic connection we had would span the remainder of both our careers, and beyond.

One thing that baffled and frustrated both Frank and me was that the entire Applications group shared use of one Digital Equipment (DEC) computer terminal and a single dot matrix printer. Compounding this poor arrangement was the inconvenient hardware location in a back storage office. These tools were our lifeline to mainframe computers that ran our performance calculation software, known as the Cycle Deck. To make a performance run, something we did daily, we needed to leave our desk, information in hand, walk to the back room terminal and hope no one else was using the equipment. Talk about poor productivity!

One afternoon as we waited in queue at the terminal, Frank and I noticed the high-speed data line to our terminal was being fed through a multiplexer that had perhaps a dozen or more unused channels. The only two channels currently being used were for the terminal and the antiquated dot matrix printer. Theoretically, if we located some cables and a couple of additional terminals, we should be able to meaningfully multiply the throughput. In fact, if we could find cables of sufficient length, we might locate a terminal conveniently on our desks in the main office area.

I guess that's one way Frank and I really complemented one another. We both liked to make things happen. While on one of our main plant visits, Frank and I convinced an Engineering manager to "loan" us two terminals, and we also located some very long cables. Returning to the office, we spent our lunch hour suspending cables by paper clips from the drop ceiling tiles to our desks. In about an hour, Frank and I had the first two desktop terminals in Applications Engineering, instantly catapulting us into the "modern age." Unfortunately, our euphoria would be short lived.

It seems the local building electricians noticed our wiring handy work and immediately filed a grievance. The next day, Frank and I were called on the carpet by our management. A long discussion ensued, resulting in mild "reprimands," likely because our leadership recognized the sound reasoning and intent behind our actions. Maybe that is why the aggrieved electricians showed up the very next day and properly installed the wires above the drop ceiling panels. Instant productivity was now legitimized[69]. Chalk one up for the good guys!

Many other unintended misadventures, resulting from good intentions, punctuated both Frank's and my careers. While they are too numerous to recount here, I will share one that briefly alarmed me, yet concluded harmlessly. Our Applications section manager, who reported to the general manager, JK, was about 6 feet, 4 inches tall and quite husky, yet he spoke in an uncharacteristic high-pitched tone that was in sharp contrast to his massive frame. Up until this point, I had minimal contact with JK, and I don't think he even knew who I was.

I was working a large desalination project bidding for the Middle East. The project involved multiple MS9001E[70] gas turbines, and site conditions

---

69 Realizing the huge productivity benefit, our management soon arranged for everyone in the group to have desktop terminals.

70 At the time the MS9001E was rated about 120 MW and was our largest 50 Hz gas turbine.

dictated use of totally enclosed water-to-air cooled (TEWAC)[71] generators. While TEWAC generators helped overcome challenges presented by environmental contaminants, they can be performance limiting in very hot climates where adequate chilled cooling water is not available[72]. Such was the case here, as the combination of high ambient temperature, a restrictive generator power factor and relatively high cooling water temperatures all worked to our disadvantage. Since GE had no larger generator to offer for this application, to avoid having our bid rejected, our salesman asked me to obtain a quotation for a larger competitor generator. Although this was highly unusual and certainly not our normal practice, I complied with the request.

Somehow, the quotation of a non-GE generator came to JK's attention. Very late one afternoon, I was summoned to his office. Now, for a bit of context here: At this point in my career, being called into a senior GE manager's office was not an everyday event—probably something akin to being summoned to the principal's office in school. Usually, there were very negative connotations associated with such visits.

Upon my arrival, without even a greeting, JK began reprimanding me for supporting use of a non-GE generator on a major GE bid. In very colorful—but not obscene—language, JK lectured me on why this was one of the worst things anyone could do. Whenever I tried to speak, I was simply cut off in mid-sentence. In the midst of his tantrum, JK actually summoned his secretary, a very competent, elderly woman named Joan, instructing her to contact payroll and immediately process my employment termination. Really? I was completely dumbfounded. Luckily, I don't think Joan took any action that night as it was already quite late and there was little chance she could reach anyone in payroll. Also, she probably knew JK much better than I did and was assuming he'd cool down by morning.

Obviously, this was a harrowing episode, and I left that evening not knowing what to expect. The following day, with my manager and his manager both briefed on the situation, I spoke to our GE lead salesman. None of us was very pleased about the incident, but all assured me they would follow up with JK. Well, I don't know what was discussed or said, but later

---

71 In deserts or other tainted environments, TEWAC generators often were used to minimize intrusion of contaminant particles.

72 Customer-required performance guarantees at 35C (95F) using very restrictive 0.80 pf.

that afternoon, JK flabbergasted me yet again. This time he called direct, another "first" for me. In what was the most unbelievable turn of events, a now very polite JK apologized for his flare-up and assured me I was doing a great job and would continue to be employed. Apparently, he had even taken time to read my personnel file as he noted that we were both RPI alumni. Henceforth, he said, we would now be "buddies." Can you beat that? It was probably not the best way to get my name known by the section manager, but it certainly got me noticed.

I never did get to exploit my newfound "buddy" connection, however. Not long after establishing my new bond, JK became ill. His illness progressed quite rapidly, apparently combining with other underlying medical conditions and resulting in his premature death. Rest in peace, JK.

Just weeks after our terminal wiring incident, Frank Brooks found himself "gifted" with a Digital Equipment Rainbow personal computer (PC). Instead of a simple "dumb" terminal, Frank now had a programmable desktop computer at his fingertips. The PC had been delivered to a certain manager who simply could not justify keeping it, so he awarded Frank custody. Little did either of us realize the incredible impact this seemingly minor transaction would unleash.

Bear in mind, the digital revolution that was happening during the 1980s would lead to major productivity upheavals. Apple, IBM and others were rapidly developing PCs. Home versions were being offered by Commodore, Atari and even Timex. It was an exciting time as PCs were getting smaller, faster, easier to use and less expensive. Both Frank and I eagerly jumped on that bandwagon as home PC enthusiasts.

With the Rainbow PC now at his desk, Frank began developing code to help streamline some of our many tedious application tasks. In what must be one of his single biggest contributions ever, Frank developed a shell program to simplify and standardize inputs to the Fortran-based Cycle Deck[73]. The Cycle Deck was the source code for all gas turbine performance calculations and, when properly executed, provided the basis for performance guarantees to customers. Prior to Frank's program, the Cycle Deck used an antiquated system of numeric codes and punctuation for input. Users would have to

---

73 GE's gas turbine performance was calculated from time-sharing code originally written in 1960s-era FORTRAN code. The reference to "deck" was a carryover from the IBM punch card decks used to submit input to the computer.

carefully translate from this unfriendly format, often introducing errors in the process. Frank modified inputs into plain language, making the shell program do the numeric input conversions, thereby reducing input errors and simultaneously streamlining the entire process.

The shell code not only improved data inputs, but it also was able to modify the raw outputs into a customer-friendly report format. Users could now easily select appropriate performance margin levels, as well as convert all data to desired units, such as Btu or kW. Not only did this save a tremendous amount of time, it also eliminated countless conversion mistakes. Further, it eliminated the need for our administrative assistants to re-type this information, as the new format was suitable for direct transmission to customers.

Along the way, I encouraged and assisted Frank as he tirelessly kept adding new features to the code. Probably my biggest contribution was testing/troubleshooting. In other words, I was very good at "breaking" Frank's latest beta shell code versions. Pandora's box had now been opened, and things would never be the same again.

The code development itself took on a life of its own, even though our management was initially skeptical. All resistance ended one day when Frank, acting as temporary manager, was called into our general manager's office. Apparently, someone had provided a customer with two different performance guarantees for the same test conditions. When Frank explained the anomaly, he also mentioned how his new shell program could eliminate the problem. Immediately, Frank was authorized to "make that happen."

In my opinion, Frank never received proper recognition from GE for his phenomenal efforts—much of it done on his own time, after completing his actual assigned work projects. There is just no way to properly convey the contribution this shell program made to the Applications team in particular and the overall business as well. Just in terms of productivity alone, the code literally chopped hours of work out of every Application engineers' schedule. When you factor in the improvement in repeatability, error reduction and accuracy over the former process, the impact was off the charts.

Well, if the overall business didn't properly recognize Frank, certainly he distinguished himself among his peers and immediate leaders. In what I feel is a lasting tribute, right up to the time of my own retirement, the performance group that inherited Frank's code continues to follow most of our same logic and report format developed in the late 1980s. This was simply an amazing productivity contribution, the likes of which is rarely seen. Little did we realize how critical the newly pioneered productivity was going to become. The winds of change were constantly blowing within GE, and a huge storm was about to descend upon us.

CEO Jack Welch was again flexing his muscles, imposing his imprint on the company. His mantra was for every business to be No. 1 or 2—or be gone. Jack was determined that he would "not allow" subpar profits, so to address the Gas Turbine department's shortfalls in the mid-1980s, he brought in a strong-armed vice president, I'll call RN. Immediately, RN announced that he was going to "streamline" things, and he introduced his own mantra, stating that "cost walks." Translation: People were going to be laid off.

RN held an "all-employee" meeting one day in a Schenectady auditorium. The message was that the turbine business had peaked years ago and now was the decline, so downsizing was imminent. Then, emphasizing his point that profitability was his only goal, RN made a statement I shall never forget: He said, "We are in the money business, not the turbine business."

RN's words reverberated in my head. How could a GE leader make such a statement? The only thing that matters is the bottom line? No mention whatsoever of the customer. Right then and there I lost total respect for the man as his words numbed every cell in my body. I didn't know what was ahead for GE, nor for me, but I left that meeting feeling about as low as I had ever felt regarding my future with the company.

Soon after that meeting, rumors began to fly about the numbers of folks to be laid off. Flashbacks to my prior Combustion layoff experience rushed into my head. Would I be going down that road again? Everything came to a head one Friday afternoon. Why do these awful events always happen on a Friday?

A well-known and respected industry expert, I'll call LT, had now replaced JK as our section level manager. On this terrible day, LT came to our Rotterdam Industrial Park facility from his downtown Schenectady office, joining our Applications managers in what was an ominous closed-door meeting. Shortly thereafter, several engineers from our Applications team were individually summoned to the meeting room. One by one they entered the office, emerging shortly thereafter with looks of shock, disdain and sadness. It was an excruciating afternoon, as my cubicle was just outside the office, and I watched several co-workers repeat the cycle. Although nothing had been formally announced, we all understood that the layoffs were happening.

At that point, I had only been in Applications a couple of years. I don't know how I survived that cut, but somehow I did. I suppose my immediate leaders saw something that made them keep me and terminate others. At the time, I felt no satisfaction from surviving the layoff. Perhaps it's something akin to survivors' guilt. Those of us who were left sometimes wondered who was luckier—those who were cut and moved on to other things, or those of us left behind.

Over the next two years our salaries were literally frozen. In lieu of merit raises, GE issued minimal, one-time lump-sum distributions, based on performance. As I recall, the first year amounted to $500 and the second year it was $1,000. This cash payment did not even count toward our pension, nor was it matched in our retirement savings program.

During those two years and continuing for the next several years, my coworkers and I worked tirelessly to help get our business back to profitability. Certainly this was not a pleasant time. Few, if any of us, ever recovered financially from these two "lost" years because future salaries were always incremental above current pay levels. I suppose this was GE's way of enticing people to "move on," and many of my associates did just that.

After the second year of the "salary freeze," while facing increasing turnover and slumping morale, the company instituted a first-of-a-kind "bonus" program tied to business performance. Being the loyal, hardworking and innovative workforce that we were, we hit and exceeded our escalating business targets each year thereafter. As our business profitability increased, the bonus amounts reflected our progress and actually started to become meaningful. However, after about the fourth or fifth year, just as the bonus amounts were becoming more significant, the company abruptly ended the program.

Paralleling our business' return to profitability, my career seemed to accelerate as well. As my manager, Bob Gessner, was nearing retirement, he asked if I'd be interested in taking his place on what was then called the Electric Utility Committee[74]. This committee was part of a larger professional organization known as the International Gas Turbine Institute (IGTI), which I believe is still the largest branch of the American Society of Me-

---

74 The committee has since been renamed the Electric Power Committee.

chanical Engineers (ASME). Bob represented GE on the Electric Utilities Committee by chairing its Legislative and Regulatory subcommittee.

I was honored and excited at this prestigious opportunity. Not only was participation in a respected international professional organization a tremendous exposure-broadening opportunity, but it played directly into my passion for improving the environment.

As an IGTI committee member, I had unbelievable opportunities to participate in major turbine conferences across North America and Europe while connecting with other industry experts. My volunteer work on the committee included reviewing technical papers, chairing technical presentation sessions at conferences, and regularly participating in bi-annual committee meetings.

At those meetings, I formalized Bob Gessner's practice of reporting on key legislative and regulatory topics related to gas turbines. Generally, I relied on my personal experiences from Applications projects, but soon found that I needed to supplement my relatively narrow exposure. I did so by contacting others from GE who were working more directly on these issues. My information quests introduced me to a fellow named Marv Schorr, then a senior environmental engineer based with a GE consulting group in Schenectady.

Almost immediately, Marv and I recognized that we had a special bond and we eventually organized an informal team with a few other like-minded experts who regularly communicated with industry peers, leadership teams, customers and regulators. We worked hard to synthesize what often were misunderstood, complicated technical issues, into clear, concise summaries to help drive better decisions by all. At the end of the day, we educated regulators and customers alike allowing them to make environmental decisions based on solid technical information. I very much enjoyed traveling with Marv to give our seminars at conferences or directly to regulators across the US. More about this later.

Bob Gessner did one other really great thing for my career before he retired, although neither of us realized it at the time. A gigantic questionnaire consisting of more than 300 technical questions was forwarded to our Applications group from the Sales team. The questions originated from a key strategic GE customer, a very large southeast utility. In essence, this customer was the GE equivalent of a casino's whale[75], and the questions were a precursor to a more formal request for proposal (RFP) the customer was developing for a major new combustion turbine project. Instructions accompanying the questionnaire requested written answers to the questions within one week, followed by a multiday technical discussion at the customers' offices.

After carefully considering this rather unusual request, Bob called me into his office to discuss a plan of attack. Clearly, the amount of information being requested was quite voluminous, so Bob asked me to coordinate the overall GE technical responses. Inputs would be solicited from across our entire Engineering team. Given the tight timeline and importance of this customer, Bob and our subsection manager, RA, both committed to personally assist me. All three of us had a long teleconference with the GE customer account executive, who I'll refer to as BB. In our phone call, BB shared other insights about the customer and the upcoming project, and I immediately felt more comfortable when hearing this valuable background information. I hoped the positive vibe I sensed when speaking over the phone to BB would prove out when we met in person.

Soon I was pulling together material and responses to questions. I would estimate that initially between Bob, RA and myself, we could only answer about one-third of the total questions. The three of us began making calls to other GE organizations seeking answers to the more difficult inquiries. For the next week all I did from early morning until late evening was work on questionnaire responses. As the reply deadline approached, our administrative assistant began typing up the responses on her new Wang word processor[76]. The GE response itself became a rather voluminous 150-page document. Some questions had very brief answers, others could be addressed in brochures, while still others would require face-to-face discussions.

In retrospect, I probably learned more about our GE equipment from this assignment that I did from just about any other single project. Addressing so many questions and spanning such broad technical areas brought me into contact with virtually every engineering expert across our business. It

---

75 In gambling parlance, a whale is a very high-stakes player. Because these are the most lucrative customers, casinos spend a commensurate amount of time and attention on them.

76 PCs with word processing had not yet made it to our desktops.

was a really terrific education, but it was done under serious time constraints and had to be delivered in a pressure-packed live meeting.

The entire effort was much more than just answering questions. I needed to fully comprehend each answer, since I was going to be "on the hot seat", delivering responses directly to the customer. Further, I not only needed a deep technical understanding, but I needed to appreciate the overall philosophical approach embodied in GE's gas turbine generator package design. The questions, too, were enlightening, as they provided valuable insight into the mindset of one of our most sophisticated customers.

I ended up spending three very long days answering questions posed by a cross-functional team of customer technical experts. I was most appreciative that our subsection manager, RA, spent one of those days with me covering some of the deeper philosophical topics. In addition, an Electrical Controls manager, Bill Rowen, spent one day bolstering my electrical, controls and instrumentation knowledge. The final day I handled alone. At the conclusion, I received a gratifying comment when the customer lead person mentioned how impressed he was with my perseverance and ability to handle such a wide range of topics. Although there were still a number of unanswered questions that none of us could answer, I promised and did follow up on those.

Those three days with this very sophisticated customer launched a long-term relationship that would span several years of my career. Not long after we concluded that marathon meeting, the customer issued an official RFP. Due to my initial involvement, I was assigned to the project. About three years from my initial customer involvement—and countless meetings, calls and letter responses—GE won a most competitive bid for one of the largest gas turbine simple cycle peaking plants in the US. Rumor has it that the final project award decision was made on a golf course between GE and the customer executives. While I never received formal confirmation of that rumor, in the end the customer purchased 16 of our largest 60 Hz gas turbines[77]. By yet another unusual coincidence, these turbines were equipped with multi-nozzle quiet combustors[78]—the very same MNQC system I had successfully field tested during my Combustion role about eight years earlier.

---

77 At the time this was the MS7001EA product.

78 Years after the successful MNQC field test I ran in 1981, GE finally commercialized this product.

Winning that project earned me quite a bit of positive recognition from my peers and management. My new manager, Jim H, nominated me for my first-ever significant managerial award. The citation, received in March 1989, reads: "For outstanding support of the [customer name] proposal resulting in a $250 million order for TTD[79]." The award consisted of a net $2,000 cash bonus and included a luncheon presentation and professional photograph with our general manager, JP, along with my manager and his boss, RA. It was an amazing and humbling experience.

Over the next two years, during project execution, I was regularly invited to meetings involving this prominent customer. Although I was not formally a part of the requisition team, I continued to be intimately involved on all performance and emission matters at the direct request of the customer. In many ways, I had become an internal GE go-to person for this client. I was even asked to accompany the customer to provide "expert" testimony for their site air permit application. Air permit assistance was becoming a specialty area for me, and it dovetailed nicely with my regulatory/legislative roles at ASME/IGTI. Further, it complemented my newfound association with GE regulatory expert Marv Schorr, along with the knowledge I gained during my five years working in Combustion. Everything really does happen for a reason.

Our customer insisted upon many "non-standard" design changes to our equipment. The special requests, often requiring my personal involvement, sent ripples across GE networks, causing all kinds of perturbations for the factory folks working the MS7001EA production line which often required my personal involvement. To this day, the 16 MS7001EAs purchased by this customer are the only units ever built with fully sized electric 1200 HP starting motors. Incorporating this larger motor (an 800 HP[80] motor was standard) required nearly a total redesign of the entire accessory base. GE would ordinarily never undertake such a unique special design, but exceptions were made on this large multi-unit order for a strategic customer. No, I didn't make any new friends in Manufacturing, but I helped to assure we fulfilled this contract as promised.

---

79 Turbine Technology Department was then the latest name for our business segment.

80 The 800 HP starting motor regularly operates well over rated current during the relatively short start cycle. Given frequent starts by these peaking units, the customer insisted on a fully rated motor.

While this client was very demanding and GE often struggled with the special requests, in the end I think the customer ultimately received a superior set of equipment. Everyone on the team, especially me, learned a great deal from the experience. My involvement with the project spanned for about five years, right up through plant commercial commissioning. Nearly a decade later, I would receive a pleasant reminder of just how highly the customer thought of me. More about that later. Meanwhile, there were still more mountains for me to climb.

Another major event took place around the same time. While it's not directly career related, it did significantly impact both my professional and personal life. In the spring of 1986 I used some of my accumulated airline reward miles to take my dad on his lifelong dream trip to Hawaii. Neither Dad nor I could have ever imagined what a life-changing event this trip would entail.

After seven wonderful days covering touristy Honolulu, we traveled to Maui for a somewhat different and quieter experience in the Kaanapali beach area. On the very last day, we had a late afternoon departure flight back to Honolulu, so we decided to take one last morning ocean swim prior to beginning the long trek home. That decision changed both our lives, along with that of our entire family, forever.

During our swim, a rogue wave appeared out of nowhere and quickly grew to perhaps 15 to 20 feet. Before either of us could react, the massive wave slammed us both hard into the steep[81] Maui beach. Instinctively my hands and arms moved forward to brace my fall, which likely prevented any serious injury. I struggled to catch my breath and regain my footing, and it took all my strength to just hold my position against the now rapidly receding water.

Dad was not so fortunate. As I soon discovered, he had landed flat on his back. When I spotted him several yards away, he was struggling to breathe, while attempting to stand against the powerful force of retreating water. I stumbled toward him and tried to help him up, but frankly, if it wasn't for help from a couple of nearby folks, I wouldn't have been able to get him safely on the beach.

---

81 The Hawaiian Islands, formed primarily by volcanic activity, actually have relatively steeply sloped beaches, which can enhance wave impacts, a fact I was not aware of prior to this incident.

At Maui Memorial Hospital, Dad was diagnosed with two broken thoracic vertebrae, along with a host of other injuries,—and he was suffering from shock. As I reviewed the three-dimensional MRI images along with his doctors, what startled everyone was that the injury occurred in such a way that miraculously Dad's spinal cord remained completely intact. His doctor, who had seen thousands of similar injuries, was astounded because such severe fractures always resulted in some degree of paralysis. Astonishingly, Dad had no paralysis whatsoever. Somehow, our guardian angels had been watching over us both—again.

The next month was quite a roller coaster ride, as I struggled alone, thousands of miles from home, making dozens of decisions. Almost everywhere I turned there were seemingly insurmountable problems to tackle. To this day, I really can't say what got me through that month. It might have simply been sheer determination, but I know there must have been some divine intervention that sustained me during the low points.

Dad's recovery would span years, but miraculously, the injury healed itself without requiring surgery. Ironically, as is often the case, some good actually resulted from this terrible event. Over most of his life, Dad had been a smoker who had unsuccessfully tried to quit. Now, as a result of his ocean accident, the habit had been broken, and he would never again touch another cigarette. While I was pleased that Dad would no longer be a smoker, I wished his habit could have been broken by a less extreme method.

Dad's recovery was an inspiration as I observed his positive attitude, but it also was a wakeup call, driving home the point that there really are no guarantees for tomorrow. Now fully understanding that everything can change in an instant, I had a new sense of appreciation for family priorities. No matter what lay ahead in my career or whatever new opportunities would come my way, family would always come first.

Chapter 10

FUN IN THE SUN

FOLLOWING THE BIG CUSTOMER ORDER win, my career seemed to accelerate further. Both Frank Brooks and I both were promoted to Technical Leaders (TLs) within the group. Frank continued to hone his Cycle Deck shell program, adding tremendous new capabilities and functionality. As a TL, he expanded upon his coding work, leading an informal productivity sub-team while still supporting new bid activity. I maintained a more traditional role supporting our Sales teams, but now had added responsibilities to assign projects, coach and even evaluate others on our team. Taking full advantage of my new authority, I often assigned myself some of the more unusual and challenging projects, especially when trips to desirable locations might be involved.

I wasn't the only person in my family to pursue science or technology as a career. My sister Elaine and three first cousins followed suit. Alan Demania, one year my junior, oldest son of my dad's eldest sister Mary, began working at GE as a technical specialist. Taking advantage of GE's tuition refund program, he earned his engineering degree by attending Union College part time, eventually joining the professional ranks. When the inevitable GE downturn hit, he took a seven-year hiatus, working for a defense contractor in Ohio. Ultimately, he returned to GE, finishing his own fine career in a turbine engineering design role. Before retiring from GE, he had designed one of the largest last stage steam turbine buckets ever built.

On the maternal side of the family, my cousin Karen "Gynger" Frick also attended Union College, studying Mechanical Engineering. She followed her own calling and immediately joined GE's Technical Sales Program where she enjoyed a successful career in Turbine Commercial Sales. For several years she was based near London, England, where she met and married her husband, Brian Connolly, himself a GE field service engineer. Following the birth of their two daughters, she left GE, assuming leadership of her dad's small, yet very successful custom window treatment and radiator enclosure business.

About a decade behind me, yet another cousin, Steven Davi, only son of my dad's younger brother Salvatore, also pursued a technology career. Steve attended Worcester Polytechnic Institute and later Northeastern, earning BS and MS degrees, respectively, in computer science. Today he has risen to a lofty engineering executive leadership role with a Boston area company.

Rounding out my generation, my sister, Elaine studied medical sciences, eventually becoming a Professor of Nursing. The point here is that, despite any obstacles, it really is possible to advance yourself. The key theme is that a solid education is crucial. It does take effort, but my own story was not unique. While not quite a majority of my generation, five of us made it through the gauntlet and successfully pursued science/technology-related careers.

Throughout my career, the GE technical groups I was associated with were predominantly male. Women were not often encouraged to pursue technical careers, nor was the work environment supportive of their development. However, during my career I had the privilege to work with three very memorable female pioneers who successfully crashed the gender barrier.

The first, and in my mind the most memorable woman I encountered, was M. Jeanne Place, who had worked her way into a leadership position as head of Gas Turbine Compressor Aerothermal Engineering. This was no small accomplishment for a woman in the 1970s. Soft spoken, gracious, and very intelligent, she was always pleasant and easy to work with. I worked with her on a Greenville test stand, where we were experimenting with opening the inlet guide vanes[82] on an early 7E gas turbine. Combustion assigned me to watch for any unusual combustor dynamic impact as the guide vanes were opened.

I was thrilled when Jeanne invited me to crawl inside the compressor bell mouth with her to manually measure and verify the actual guide vane angles. Her thoroughness, attention to detail and willingness to get her hands dirty were very impressive to me. She earned my respect that day and never lost it throughout both of our careers. Probably there is no more lasting tribute to

---

82 Inlet guide vanes were movable blades that were used to help meter the airflow into the axial compressors. They were typically closed during startup to help prevent compressor surge, but then opened as the unit came up to speed. More open position meant more airflow through the entire turbine, thus more available power.

Jeanne's work than the fact that GE compressors are recognized throughout the industry as some of the finest in the world. Jeanne, it was my pleasure to know and work with you for many years[83].

Betty Lou Bailey, the second of the three pioneering women I wish to mention, might be considered a bit eccentric. Often you could see her biking across the GE plant on nice days, long skirt flapping in the breeze. When I first met her, she was conducting emissions compliance testing on our diffusion flame gas turbines. Recall that these early units used water or steam injection to control NOx emissions. Betty usually would drop by to confirm control settings and verify guarantee emissions levels at a particular site prior to heading into the field. Years of testing at customer sites made Betty keenly aware of being properly prepared. Problems in the field involving compliance testing were especially onerous as they could shut down a machine, potentially incurring regulatory fines and always be guaranteed to upset customers. Certainly I identified with and respected Betty for confronting these pressure-packed situations with a level head and always driving to a satisfactory result. I'm sure she likely encountered gender harassment of some kind along the way, especially considering the rarity of women working such roles. So Ms. Betty Lou, hats off to you for bravely battling through the many challenges you faced.

Nancy Fitzroy was the third and probably the most widely known of the three ground-breaking women, I knew, who distinguished themselves in the male-dominated GE turbine business. Her gender surely was not the only factor facilitating Nancy's ability to separate herself from any engineering stereotype. Nancy exhibited a rare combination of intelligence, gregarious personality, and approachability that, when combined with her bright golden blonde hair, always drew attention in a gathering. By the time I met her, she already had achieved a long and distinguished GE career spanning many roles involving heat transfer, fluid dynamics and a host of other technologies.

Late in her GE career, Nancy worked in a consulting role with GE Marketing for Energy and Environmental Programs. While I only briefly interacted with her on environmental topics, our encounters were still memo-

---

83 While writing this book, I encountered Jeanne, long retired and nearing 90 years of age, at one of the informal weekly Gas Turbine retiree lunches. Jeanne's mind was still as sharp as ever, and I enjoyed reminiscing briefly with her. Sadly, in February 2018, we were informed that Jeanne passed away. Everyone who knew her was certainly touched by this very special woman who will be warmly remembered.

rable to me. When I discovered Nancy was both an accomplished fixed wing and helicopter pilot, she was instantly elevated to an even higher stature in my mind. Rarely, if ever, did I meet a fellow aviator that I didn't admire. Not long after we met, Nancy attained further distinction as she was elected the first female president of the American Society of Mechanical Engineers. By any measure this was an extraordinary milestone for her, GE and the society itself. I was most fortunate to meet and work with Nancy, Betty Lou and Jeanne, each very distinctive, in different fields of expertise, but who each added some thought-provoking perspectives to my own career.

Back to my new TL role, where "fuel of the week" questions had become a routine occurrence. More specifically, customers transmitted a constant variety of fuel compositions asking, "Can we burn this in your turbine?" Questions typically involved suitability of either "waste" or other residual process gases or liquids as a potential fuel for our gas turbines. Often, there was an inadequate quantity of fuel to fully operate one of our gas turbines. This meant that I had to manually determine a proper fuel mixture by blending whatever fuel the customer submitted with a more traditional fuel, such as methane, to obtain a suitable composition. My solid chemistry knowledge and years of Combustion experience were still paying dividends. Those qualifications made me a magnet for fuel-related inquiries, which regularly filtered in from across GE's worldwide sales network. I certainly enjoyed the challenges these posed and derived satisfaction from being able to address these inquiries.

Every project I worked always seemed to entail an environmental aspect. Whether it was noise, air emissions or water usage, each customer had unique eco concerns. Navigating both our customers and regulators through this complex decision maze was a challenging endeavor. By delivering concise, fact-based responses, my colleagues and I helped countless customers and regulators better understand GE equipment capabilities, thereby helping drive a more rational decision-making process.

Since my college days, when I first read Rachel Carson's classic environmental book "Silent Spring" I had been an advocate for planet Earth. Now, in addition to being an advocate, I was positively engaged in action for the cause. My environmental efforts, particularly alongside dedicated colleagues like Marv Schorr, provided some of the most worthwhile and personally rewarding accomplishments of my career.

Exotic travel continued to be part of my Application Engineering experience. When a potential trip to Australia came up, I was told to get a multiyear visa to visit the island nation. Unfortunately the trip was cancelled, but little did I realize having that visa would open the door to another opportunity about a year later. Sure enough another important customer meeting arose in the beautiful western Australian city of Perth. At the very last minute, my boss, who had planned to take the trip himself, needed to cancel. As it turned out, I was the only available person able to respond on 24 hours' notice, with a valid visa. Things just have a way of working out.

So off I went, leaving on my birthday in mid-January, which just happened to be the middle of summer down under. It was a wonderful, if exhausting experience. The Sales folks, along with our Japanese bidding partners, even had an opportunity to continue our meetings in Sydney for several days, affording me a fantastic opportunity to see some of that gorgeous city. Of all the places I visited, none seemed to compare to Australia, where the people were fantastic, the atmosphere was vibrant and I even understood the language, or at least most of it. While GE did not win the prime order on that job, ultimately our European Business Associates group was awarded the project as they could better meet the unique wiring and electrical codes. Chalk up another win!

Somewhere in this general timeframe, in my Applications role, I met a long-tenured GE engineer named Saul Kaplan. The man would ultimately become a highly valued teacher, colleague and friend. Everything about Saul was unique, including his title of Principal Engineer[84]. Such titles, mainly used for honorary purposes, were a rarity for GE at the time. In Saul's case, I believe it was the business' way of recognizing him as the exceptional, highly experienced technical expert he was, without encumbering him as a manager with direct reports.

Saul was a living version of "Wikipedia" long before that reference ever became the internet phenomenon it is today. His deep technical expertise was born from an impressive series of prior technical positions, many from other GE businesses such as Space Systems Business in Valley Forge, Pennsylvania. While my early dealings with Saul were quite limited, once he joined our Applications team, I had daily contact with him. I soon recognized his

84 Much later in my career, GE re-defined the position of principal engineer as one of three titled Engineering positions (consulting and chief were the others), designed to offer an alternative to the traditional management career path for valued technical contributors.

amazing ability to provide sound and complete answers to even the most unusual queries. As our acquaintance developed, I became attuned to his unusual sense of humor. Often, he would test my knowledge by floating a purposely distorted or even preposterous answer to my queries, just to gauge my reaction. Only after successful demonstration of an acceptable level of understanding would he reveal the true answer.

Saul had a tremendous willingness to share his abundant knowledge, and I valued his opinions and observations on a wide variety of topics, including the leadership and direction of our company. In our private conversations, Saul always "told it like it is" without regard to political correctness, and I respected his openness and honesty.

Saul and I were probably as unlikely a set of characters to become close colleagues and friends as you can imagine. Saul was my senior by some 20-plus years. We were of completely different faiths and ethnicities. I was much more gregarious and loved constantly meeting new people plus traveling to exotic locales. Saul was much more introverted, primarily focused on our business, technical work and family without many outside distractions. I suspect his demeanor during our years together was related to severe health conditions, which limited his activities. Despite debilitating medical issues, I never once heard him complain, except to mention his dislike of monthly "pissing contests" (Saul-speak for office visits) with his cardiologist. I came to accept and value my bond with this trusted co-worker, friend and teacher as another anomaly of my unusual career path.

When responding to questions, Saul strived for completeness at the expense of brevity. In fact, his responses, particularly to the young Sales trainees, were commonly referred to as "epistles." Some jokingly referred to him as a "man of a few thousand words". It was humorous to observe young trainees struggle with his voluminous technical responses to a single question, which could be 20-plus typed pages. My files were packed with many useful legacy documents and guidelines, courtesy of Saul.

However, my most treasured memories of Saul are the many Saulisms[85] he left us with. These were a constant source of comic relief in the pressure-packed atmosphere in which we worked. Below I've listed what I consider

---

85 This was our shorthand reference to Saul's many pithy expressions and observations that became legendary in my world.

to be the most memorable of these, along with a brief explanation of each. While these quips probably are most appreciated by colleagues who heard them in context, I'm hoping other readers can relate to and appreciate this distinctive brand of humor.

Critics to contributor ratio—To my knowledge, Saul invented this arbitrary measurement that was an attempt to quantify the number of people who actually did meaningful work (contributors) compared to the total number of folks who pretended to lead, simply stood idly by watching, or downright impeded progress (critics). Saul established the following values for this ratio: <=0.25 is OK, >0.5 is terrible, >1.0 forget it. Saul would often state that GE is in the 1.0 range.

Let me digress meaningfully—This meant that Saul was about to launch into a long tirade to add context or meaning to one of his responses.

I have to speak to management about increasing my food stamp allowance—This was a thinly veiled derogatory comment on the minimal salary increases GE had been giving, particularly during the salary freeze periods.

I don't get incentive compensation, otherwise I'd do it—Saul would use this brush-off comment, often in jest, when asked to tackle a very challenging task involving considerable effort and time.

If we don't get this task done by tomorrow, life as we know it will not come to an end—This was Saul's response to outrageous deadlines, often imposed upon Applications, typically in conjunction with last-minute complex Sales requests. Despite his defiant tone, Saul often worked extraordinary hours to meet these demanding deadlines.

My boss walks on water, his boss created water—Saul reserved this response for individuals who name-dropped senior leaders, hoping the name might instill an added sense of urgency to a particular request.

I'll have to first check with my "supreme commander"—Before making any time/travel commitments, Saul always had to check in with his "supreme commander," aka his wife.

I don't talk to him because he works on the wrong side of the exhaust plenum—Saul was a tried and true gas turbine guy, so he often maintained a friendly rivalry with those who worked the steam (bottoming cycle) side of our business.

You are speaking about an area that's "outside of my playpen" — This reference was made to responsibility areas beyond Saul's organizational jurisdiction.

That person is a "walking liability" —Saul made this unabashed reference to those deemed to be incompetent or troublesome individuals.

All he/she is good for is causing hemorrhoids—A reference reserved for the most obnoxious individuals, similar to "walking liabilities" or critics previously described.

What you're speaking about is basically known as "numerical masturbation" —Saul used this classic description for folks who, in his opinion, improperly used statistics to demonstrate a very controversial point.

If you don't stop pestering me, I'll bring you up on charges of "management brutality" —Whenever management would interrupt Saul, in futile attempts to urge him to work harder/faster, Saul would amusingly use this expression to brush them aside.

XXX was invented to be the most user-malevolent program known to man—XXX referred to any new, non-intuitive, computer software imposed upon us. When he was at wits end, Saul's frustration would boil over and henceforth would designate such programs as "the most user-hostile" or "user-malevolent" known to man. Calls to the IT Help Desk, aka the "Hinder Desk", would often follow.

Long before it was widely recognized, Saul observed how GE CEO Jack Welch was "turning GE into a bank." The analysis was spot on as Welch diverted huge sums of money away from the core "smokestack" businesses, like Power, in favor of "cleaner" financial ventures involving GE Capital. I regularly speculated with Saul how shocked and disappointed Edison and Steinmetz would be if they knew of Welch's decisions. Yet as profits and stock price rose to record levels in the 1990s, Wall Street and the business media continued to idolize the GE CEO. Ultimately—a decade or so later—things would change drastically, nearly destroying the company.

Undoubtedly Saul contributed very positively to my development on many levels, and I'm very grateful for knowing him. His shared wisdom certainly broadened my awareness and made me a better engineer. Both attributes would be needed to handle future challenges destined to come my way. Rest in peace, old friend, and thanks for all you taught me.

Out of the blue, another mega project arose. This memorable opportunity involved a major new combined cycle project in Florida. GE had lost an earlier project to this very customer, so everyone involved was asked to bring their "A" game, as this was designated a "must win" order. Our front line 60 Hz MS7001F turbines were to be the prime movers in a classic two-on-one[86] combined cycle configuration, in combination with our newly introduced D11 steam turbines.

After bid evaluations, GE was invited to bid clarification and ultimately to contract negotiations with the customer at its Florida offices. The painstaking negotiations carried on for months, and I can't recall the total number of trips I made, but it must have been in the double digits. Our local GE account executive, a fellow we called Swanie, who was a pleasure to work with. On the GE headquarters sales team, I was partnered with one of my favorite salesmen, Chuck N, who directed the commercial negotiations, working closely with Swanie. Chuck N was assisted by Dan P, a relatively new proposal manager, who seamlessly integrated onto the team. Of course, the technical responsibilities fell exclusively to me. Recognizing the voluminous and specialized electrical requirements in the customer specification, I requested help and was assigned assistance from a Controls expert.

---

86 Two gas turbines with exhausts feeding via heat recovery steam generators to a single steam turbine.

The Controls person assigned to work with me was a highly experienced senior engineer named Ted Chamberlin. Although I knew Ted from prior contacts in Schenectady, we had never worked together before on an extended basis. I really don't recall who assigned Ted to work with me, but our partnership was a match made in heaven. Ted had a terrific "can do" attitude, and we meshed extremely well together. An outsider would never realize we were working our first major project together. As a technical tandem, we would be confronted with arduous electrical details embedded in the complex utility specification. Luckily, Ted had a very extensive network of expert GE contacts, and we would need every one of them on this project.

This particular Sunshine State customer had some unique and demanding electrical requirements. For instance, because some of the most frequent lightning strikes in America occur in Florida, the utility had some very explicit grounding constraints. Exploiting his network, Ted and I contacted more than a dozen experts in manufacturing centers across the US to work through these details. And grounding was merely one of hundreds of specialized requirements, all of which seemed to require contact with still more experts across the company. Integrating the new information into our existing proposal and ultimately into the project contract kept our team fully engaged for many weeks. Those weeks quickly grew into months. Make no mistake, this was a massive effort eventually involving dozens of GE personnel.

During these negotiations, our team worked long hours, which on many days extended late into the evening. Not lost to me during this period was a recognition of the sharp dichotomy between our surroundings—we were staying at a beach resort—and the pressure-packed, sometimes contentious meetings we were embroiled in each day. Nothing would drive this point home better than observing beach-clad tourists heading off for a day of fun and relaxation as our team paraded, suit and tie, to the business at hand. It sure would have been nice to take a few days off and enjoy the resort where we were staying[87]. Our local host did treat us to a couple of outstanding meals at some of his favorite establishments in the picturesque coastal Florida area, so yes we did receive a perk or two for our Herculean efforts.

---

87 Actually, I did just that at the end of one particularly long session, by staying over a night or two on my own. Remember what I said earlier about smelling the roses?

After what seemed like a never-ending series of meetings, our perseverance finally paid off and GE was at last awarded the order. I was most privileged to be part of the elite on-site team handling the face-to-face negotiations for this pivotal project. As was customary at the time, Sales typically wrote a complementary letter to our management that provided justification for our Engineering leadership to recognize us with a significant business award. Once again, I received a major management award recognizing my contribution to this huge mega-customer win.

A number of smaller projects I worked also became gratifying GE wins. In Florida alone, I participated as the technical lead for wins in Vero Beach, Gainesville, Fort Pierce, Jacksonville and Lakeland. I even worked extensively on a project for Reedy Creek Utilities, the official power provider for Disney's massive Orlando area resorts, but I can't recall if we were ultimately successful on that project or not. Still other wins were spread out across the US, from Texas to California, and I even had a fun project in Holland, Michigan. As I recall the plant owners there intended to artfully camouflage the turbine exhaust systems in classic Dutch motif by painting giant tulips on the stacks.

On the downside, there were memorable losses as well. I expended considerable effort into many of those losses, so I felt it quite personally when a competitor won an order. What was most frustrating was that most commonly we lost orders for commercial reasons[88]. One especially memorable loss involved the repowering of a defunct nuclear plant in the US heartland, using our gas turbines to generate power and provide steam energy in place of the reactor. Our GE technical team really pulled out all the stops, and we were thrilled to win the top technical evaluation from among all bidders. Ultimately, the customer insisted on an extended long-term commercial fuel price guarantee to which GE would not commit. I recall CEO Jack Welch being personally involved in the negotiations. While I'll never know exactly what went on at the executive level, the project ultimately was awarded to a competitor who provided a more favorable commercial guarantee. When learning of the outcome, Welch was livid. Rumors flew that he campaigned federal, state and local political leaders, as well as regional industry executives, in a failed attempt to pressure the customer to reconsider.

---

88 Typically, these most frequently involved onerous, one-sided terms and conditions, such as "evergreen" parts guarantees.

In recognition of our exceptional technical efforts, a senior GE sales executive decided to take the entire proposal team to an appreciation luncheon. It is the only time in my career that I can recall such an uncommon event, promptly dubbed the "losers luncheon." Despite the derogatory tag, the gesture was much appreciated by the technical team.

My Application Engineering world was rarely dull. With a handful of active projects, new bids coming in daily, plus IGTI committee duties and the occasional regulatory meetings, I had plenty on my plate. Due to the fast-paced nature and high volume of work, new people hired into the group or joined while on rotating assignment. One of those new people was a fellow named Louis Moretti. Like so many before him, Lou began his career in GE's highly regarded Installation and Services Engineering training program. As careers progress, many field service engineers desire a more geographically stable life style, which ultimately land them in more conventional roles. Such was the case with Lou, and we were most fortunate to hire him. Field engineers understand turbine equipment extremely well, from practical first-hand experience, making them extremely desirable for the gas turbine application position.

In addition to being one of the sharpest application engineers I ever worked with, Lou was a skilled communicator who seemed naturally gifted to handle difficult sales negotiations. I could always count on Lou to be fully prepared, even for the most extreme customer demands, which he handled with enviable professional poise and business acumen. He and I often shared battle stories that undoubtedly helped both of us become better at our jobs. We were fortunate to be mentored by our good friend Saul, and our shared friendship and appreciation of Saul certainly contributed to the growing bond between Lou and myself.

Lou did two separate tours of duty in Gas Turbine Applications Engineering with me for a total of six years. Even after he accepted a promotion and left the group, we continued to communicate regularly. When Lou interviewed for his second tour in Applications, I'm proud to say I was instrumental in convincing our new leadership to rehire him.

Following his second stint, Lou moved into project management and ultimately progressed to a managerial role, where he would become one of GE Power's all-time finest project managers. That's not just me talking, but is validated both by his personal record and by most everyone who worked with or for him.

At some point, too, destiny had decided that Lou and I would become best friends for life. Although we currently live more than 1,500 miles apart, we still speak regularly and visit directly when circumstances allow.

For me, there is no more valuable takeaway from my GE career than the amazing people I met and worked with along the way. Working alongside such talented and culturally diverse colleagues added an unexpected yet welcome dimension to my career that continually reinvigorated my enthusiasm. For a kid growing up in Schenectady, this was a phenomenal ride. Yet, just around the corner still more interesting projects were about to be unleashed.

Chapter 11

THREE-PEAT

NOTHING CAN ENHANCE AN APPLICATION Engineer's reputation better than an impressive string of project wins. Although all wins were team efforts, each individual contributor was held accountable and responsible for his or her part. At this point in my career, I had solidified my reputation as a technical person who could measure up to winning standards on the most important proposals.

Undoubtedly my career was augmented because I continuously pursued new learning opportunities. Each year following GE's annual performance review, I focused on improvement areas identified by my managers. Thankfully, GE offered an abundant mixture of instructional and coaching opportunities, many of which were available through the highly regarded Crotonville[89], New York executive training facility. I took full advantage of these offerings over the years. Not only did the courses broaden my knowledge, but the entire learning experience was enhanced by other GE participants representing different businesses and cultures from across the globe. The courses I completed included Project Leadership I & II, Workshop in Negotiating Skills (WINS), Modern Marketing, Management Skills Development I & II and, later in my career, New Manager Development.

Another particularly helpful training experience was the regionally offered Effective Presentation[90] (EP) course. Without question, this training was a great confidence builder, particularly for those of us involved with customer or other business presentations. Each week, students were required to deliver

---

89 Most of these courses were offered at conference centers (like Lansdowne in Virginia and Peachtree in Atlanta) or on university campuses in the eastern US, including Princeton and Fairfield. I did study New Manager Development at Crotonville.

90 In this humbling yet confidence-building course, each class elects a primary and alternate best speaker. The primary best speaker (I was the elected alternate from my class) goes on to compete at a final annual dinner speaker event for all the local participants (totaling around 90-100) plus their managers. As it turned out, the woman elected as our top class speaker competed, and she was outstanding! I was privileged to be part of this class, which made me a much better speaker.

a short speech in class on various assigned topics. Immediately following the talk, both the class and instructor provided real-time feedback. Yes, this could be a discomforting experience, yet it yielded valuable constructive criticism and helped us improve on our speaking abilities. Despite the anxiety this course caused, I found I enjoyed it much more than I originally had anticipated.

I participated in other local trainings as well, some required, some voluntary, lasting anywhere from one day to one week, depending on the subject. It never hurts to improve your skills and learn new things. Times change quickly, and you can't always anticipate where you might end up next or what skills might be needed when you get there.

In Applications, a constant flow of new and interesting people made their way through our team. Mastering a basic understanding of performance, air emissions, as well as the entire proposal process, was essential for new Technical Sales trainees. I emphatically enjoyed meeting and working with such culturally diverse folks representing ethnicities from around the globe. Amazingly, no matter the background, culture, skin color, religion or other differences, we all came together cooperatively, united by science and technology. If only the non-GE world could get along so well!

As part of the training in our group, we made use of a California project that had languished for years, locked in a constant cycle of bid and rebid. Following each bid, the project would go dormant for months, only to resurrect again whenever a new developer showed interest. The cycle became so absurd, we routinely assigned rebids to our newest trainees, which minimized consequences of any blunders, given the low likelihood of implementation. Little did anyone realize that whole line of reasoning was about to be crushed.

This cogeneration[91] project, was quite unique in that it involved replacing nearly a century-old GE steam turbine at a sugar refining plant with a unique single-shaft (gas, steam and generator on a one-shaft) power island. Both reliable electricity and steam were required by the plant, making this an ideal cogeneration application. The project was also an excellent fit for our then largest 60 Hz MS7001F gas turbine (~170 MW), which provided ample spare electricity, beyond plant needs, that could be sold to further bolster project economic viability. Almost lost in the bid-

---

91 With cogeneration, both electricity and steam are being generated by the plant. Some or all of the steam and power can be used within the plant, with excess sold as needed.

ding confusion was the significant engineering investment this complex plant would require since GE had never before built a single-shaft unit with our MS7001F gas turbine.

As luck would have it, after years of meaningless bids, the project suddenly revived and was on track to actually become an order. A major West Coast architectural engineering firm was brought in to compile a potpourri of often conflicting bid information and launch the project. Understandably, the firm requested a bid clarification meeting—one that those of us in Applications fully understood was going to be an absolute circus. Next thing I knew, I was on a California-bound flight. Years of conflicting, often mistake-laden proposals, hastily assembled by trainees, was coming to a head. Anticipating a difficult situation, especially on the electrical side, I insisted that my outstanding Controls expert, Ted Chamberlin, accompany me. Together, Ted and I headed into a simmering firestorm.

The predictable, highly contentious meeting lived up to expectations. The opportunistic engineering firm pounced on every discrepancy in our many proposals, attempting to leverage each GE miscue in its favor. It was a grueling multiday meeting, with the commercial folks struggling with contractual issues as Ted and I wrestled with the technical side. Ultimately, we created a single "conformed" document that no one was truly happy with, but was a reasonable compromise—or so we thought. Apparently, the engineering firm was not comfortable with the risk profile and, in a highly unusual move, sold its interest to yet another West Coast engineering firm.

Just a few short weeks later, Ted and I again found ourselves California bound to do a repeat performance with a new cast of characters. Complicating the situation was an added layer of specifications, introduced by the new firm, which of course needed to establish its imprint on the situation. One positive consolation: The new firm happened to have offices in downtown San Francisco, one of my favorite cities. At least we would be in a great locale for the next confrontation.

At this point, GE assigned a project manager to the job, a fellow I'll call JZ. Prior to this project, I had never met JZ. Since we had little preparation time for this meeting, we sat together on the flight and I briefed him on the overall situation. We also discussed a general strategy and some specific tactics for the upcoming negotiation. JZ's approach was very direct and pragmatic. He also had a great sense of humor, which is certainly helpful in these tense situations. I loved his attitude and could immediately sense that we would work very well together.

In all of GE, I can't imagine a better project manager for this convoluted project. JZ tackled the commercial issues one after another and set the tone for me to call the technical shots. After another week of painstaking negotiations, JZ, Ted and I had reached agreement on an updated conformed contract document with the new engineering firm. Yes, after nearly a decade of false starts, the project was really going to happen! Just as with the prior document, no one was totally pleased, but we had a reasonable framework upon which a contract could be signed.

When the long festering California cogeneration project finally became a reality, Applications fell under a new general manager, a fellow I'll call BR. Newly transferred from the Aviation group in Lynn, Massachusetts, BR knew little about the industrial turbine business[92]. During this period, Frank Brooks and I were now being routinely called into the GM office for consultations. It's not clear how much of our opinion was used in actual decision-making, but certainly our input was regularly solicited. In one memorable "experiment," BR tried to break an existing paradigm by assigning the application engineer to follow a project from proposal right through the requisition stage[93]. Of all the projects to experiment on, this single-shaft cogeneration undertaking was about as disjointed as any project could get, and I was to be the guinea pig to launch BR's new experiment.

In short order, JZ and I were appointed co-Project Managers to handle the requisition phase. JZ handled everything commercial and had overall contractual responsibility. I handled everything technical, including all technical guarantees as well as coordination between the three major GE departments—gas turbine, steam turbine and generator. Included in my technical responsibilities would be all of what was now becoming routine air emissions permit support. As I would soon discover, any large power

---

92 This was in keeping with CEO Jack Welch's belief that good management could be cross planted across businesses. At some levels or in certain functions, this may be a reasonable assumption, but in Gas Turbine Engineering, lack of understanding at the GM level was a serious shortcoming that many of us believed was harming our business.

93 Normally, Applications Engineers handed off to a separate Requisition team after order closure.

generation equipment installed in California was also subject to a host of new special seismic requirements[94] no one in our business previously seemed to be aware of.

The aforementioned seismic requirements would prove to be a very big deal that would cost GE more than $1 million and countless delays in obtaining project approvals. In breaking this new ground, I became an internal GE seismic requirement "expert" on California projects. Ultimately, I located a GE civil engineer in Schenectady named James who possessed a California professional engineer's license. Without question, James was an enormous help on this project. Still, the seismic approval efforts delayed our drawing deliverables while subsequent compliance modifications added considerable costs to our equipment. To prevent such unexpected cost and delivery impacts in the future, James and I published a California project, "Seismic Requirements White Paper," later used throughout our business as a guide on future California projects.

For the next 18 months, I regularly traveled to beautiful San Francisco for project meetings. I even made a couple of trips to the plant site itself, to witness construction progress first hand. JZ and I routinely handled a myriad of commercial and technical issues along the way. Anytime you do a "first" there are always unexpected issues, and this project was no different. Just keeping our gas, steam and generator folks all on the same page was a constant challenge. Despite the fact that we all were part of GE, at times it really felt like I was working with three different companies because each department acted so independently. I was constantly battling a two-front struggle, one with our external customer (actually the customer's engineering firm) and one internally with our gas, steam and generator departments. Hard to categorize which was more problematic as each had its own distinctive nuances.

Probably one of the biggest technical impediments on the project involved turbine wheels of our MS7001F gas turbine. Not long after introducing the 7F product line, GE discovered a problem with turbine wheel "slip" that caused serious rotor vibrations—a very serious matter impacting most of the 7F fleet. One thing I will say is that GE stepped up and made good

---

94 Due to many active faults in California, all large power projects now had to conform to unique county-driven seismic requirements. The new codes included structural and other drawing reviews requiring approval by a licensed California professional engineer.

on the repairs with minimal impact to affected customers. One testament to GE's extraordinary pains to make things right was rental of what was then the world's largest freighter aircraft known as the Antonov[95] to speed shipment of the defective turbine rotors from customer site to our repair facilities and back after modifications.

At the end of the day, GE successfully addressed the rotor issue and achieved project commercial operation on schedule. As far as I know the plant then operated successfully for many years and may still be operating today. One other post script: Despite the successful outcome on this project, experiments involving the Application Engineers following a project through the requisition phase ended. To my knowledge, the practice has never been repeated. Reality and common sense ultimately prevailed. Soon after, BR left the company in pursuit of new opportunities.

In the world outside of GE, the computer revolution continued to transform the way our work got done. Silicon chips were progressing at an exponential pace, with smaller, faster chips revolutionizing the entire industry, yet our Applications Engineering team computers were woefully behind the technology curve. Out of frustration, Frank Brooks and I once again undertook an effort to dramatically improve office productivity. Working through a local supplier, we negotiated a favorable bulk purchase for a dozen of the most advanced desktop PCs then available. As a bonus, the supplier agreed to throw in a local area network (LAN). The networking capability allowed our PCs the then unprecedented ability to exchange email messages and transfer files among our group on this system[96].

Almost immediately after our PCs were delivered and our network was activated, our IT folks caught wind of our activity. Immediately, they came down on our management, forcing another confrontation. Ultimately, we were allowed to keep the advanced PCs but were forced to surrender the network cards and LAN capability. While I fully understand and appreciate the IT perspective to uniformly construct such networks at a business level, the fact is they operated at a snail's pace. Never did IT display any sense of

---

95 This heavy lift Russian air craft was the only airplane with enough space and lift capacity capable of transporting the entire turbine rotor. We used the Antonov so much that some of us joked that our rotors earned top tier frequent flyer mileage benefits with the Russian cargo carrier.

96 In the early 1990s, there still was no common email system or internet service as we know it today, so local email and file exchange via a closed network was quite advanced and desirable.

urgency to support our needs in the fast-paced, pressure-packed world we operated in. My understanding is that part of the problem was inadequate funding, especially for infrastructure needs. Short-term profit mentality always seemed to win out against longer range infrastructure productivity. As a result, two years slipped by before we ever acquired email and file transfer capability for our desktop PCs. That was two years of lost productivity that could never be recovered. I'm sure no one was measuring that loss, but my team lived with the consequences every day.

Another major strategic project arose in the very active US Southeast region, where we previously had been successful in winning milestone orders from two major utilities. This time, one of the largest US generators had a major project that GE again had designated as a "must win." Our winning "Fun in the Sun" team from Chapter 10 was once again reunited, including my faithful Controls expert, Ted Chamberlin. Two new personalities joined the mix for this project. First was, of course, our local account executive responsible for this major utility customer, MH. As the local GE face, our account execs were critical to all such projects. Additionally, due to complexity of the overall plant design, our Schenectady-based technical team enlisted help from a senior plant electrical expert, a most capable engineer named Boris. At the risk of contradicting any prior acclimations, I have to say this was one of the finest and most capable proposal teams I was ever associated with.

Once again, negotiations spanned many difficult months. At the pivotal win-or-go-home meeting, a dramatic event occurred very early on that, in my mind, turned the job in GE's favor. Here's what happened.

The tense meeting got off on a disconcerting tone when one of the customer's lead technical folks opened the discussion on a very prickly note, essentially stating that GE completely ignored the request for quotation (RFQ) in our proposal response. As he spoke, he gestured toward two giant plant electrical One-Line diagrams sprawled on the large conference table before us. One was from the RFQ and the other from the responding GE proposal. In his opinion, GE quoted a much more expensive and elaborate plant electrical configuration than the RFQ requested. Following his rambling tirade, an uneasy silence fell over the room.

As the GE lead technical person, I was trying to quickly gather some thoughts to make an intelligent, non-emotional rebuttal. The fact was,

Boris, Ted and I, along with a much larger team of experts, had carefully reviewed the complex customer specification. Bottom line: The GE team felt the utilities' design would compromise plant reliability. So, although we had deviated from the specification, we felt our proposal offered a more reliable and fault tolerant, albeit more expensive, solution.

Before I could complete my thoughts on how best to break the deafening silence with a factual, non-emotional response, Boris stood up and approached the diagram sprawled across the conference table. With everyone staring and anxiously awaiting a reply, Boris pointed to a single central transformer feeding power to the entire plant auxiliary system. In his strong Russian accent, Boris simply asked, "Vhat vill happen if zis transformer fails?"

Silence. Total and complete silence for what seemed like minutes, but in actuality was more like 30 seconds. The customer team exchanged puzzled looks and quietly whispered among themselves. Finally, the lead customer representative asked Boris to further explain his question. Boris did so eloquently, pointing out how the transformer in question represented a single-point failure that could bring down the entire plant. As such, it created a serious reliability concern. Further, Boris explained that replacing such a large and specialized transformer likely would require months, during which the entire plant would be out of commission. Perhaps the customer planned to keep one of these expensive backup transformers in inventory? More silence followed, but body language among the customer participants indicated that Boris' point had been made, and now everyone clearly understood the magnitude of the issue.

In my estimation, Boris' humble question and the ensuing discussion changed the entire tone of the meeting. From that point on, things seemed to break our way. While I don't think anyone can really say if that plant configuration discussion ultimately decided the outcome, it clearly established credibility for GE. In any case, we left the day-long meeting with the order in hand!

Breaking with normal award tradition, whereby awards usually were presented by individual organizational management chains, our entire proposal team was nominated for, and received, a prestigious, division-wide "Key Business Initiatives" award. At the award ceremony luncheon, GE Sales Vice President Del Williamson congratulated our entire cross functional team. A professional photographer documented the occasion by capturing both group and individual photos. Everyone on the team received a customized wood-mounted bronze plaque inscribed with our name and the words "In Recognition of Outstanding Individual Achievement" directly underneath. A bust of Thomas Edison was emblazoned in the lower left corner with CEO name and title in the lower right. I proudly displayed that award in my offices for the remainder of my career. For me, this award culminated a personal "three-peat," as I now had been the lead technical Application Engineering person for three major US regional mega orders, earning prominent business awards for each. As a further compensation, I was now selected to receive company stock options. In the 1990s, with GE stock hitting record levels and recording several splits, these turned out to be quite lucrative.

During the 1990's, GE regularly held a number of invitation-only mini seminars around the globe known as State-of-the-Art (SOA) seminars. The seminars targeted local customers in a particular region where GE could showcase latest technology developments for our equipment. Eventually, following my three-peat accomplishment, I was asked to join a prestigious group of GE technical speakers, including Marv Schorr and Frank Brooks, at a number of these seminars across the US. Each of us understood that our selection to participate on this team was an outward acknowledgement of our status in the business.

A very memorable SOA seminar series was held on a two-city US western swing covering Seattle, Washington, and San Francisco, California. Following the coastal trip, I along with Marv and several other associates, headed off to Santa Fe, New Mexico, to wrap up our trip with a smaller educational seminar with the New Mexico Air Quality Bureau.

On this particular trip, I invited my mom along as well as she had never been to either Seattle, San Francisco or New Mexico. In San Francisco, the seminar took place at the beautiful and historic Sheraton Palace Hotel. Mom was most impressed, and I bought her a meal fit for a queen the night before our seminar in one of the Palace's fine dining rooms. Coincidently, this very dining room was the site where, about a decade earlier, I had dined with my aunt Gina (moms sister), while we visited her daughter (my cousin) Karen (aka Gynger), who was then herself based in San Francisco on a rotating GE assignment. Again, it's remarkable how all of these small uncanny happenings occur connecting people, places and events that span many years!

During my SOA presentation in one of the Sheraton's large ball rooms, mom unexpectedly decided to check out my talk. Her unscheduled arrival happened to coincide with me on stage giving my presentation, so I didn't notice her entering the back of a very large room filled nearly to capacity with several hundred customers. Just as well, I didn't need any added pressure or distraction. However, the local GE Sales folks, always on guard for potential competitors or uninvited guests, immediately converged. When the Sales folks learned she was my mom, they immediately found her a seat and treated her like royalty, serving her coffee and Danish. I only learned of the incident after completing my presentation and live audience questions/answers. As I joined my mom afterward, she asked me where I learned to speak so well, as she was not used to hearing me speak technical jargon before. That was the one and only time she had ever witnessed me speak professionally, so that was an added treat on what was a very fun trip.

Perhaps a year or two following the West Coast SOA trip, GE conducted a major SOA seminar in Asheville, North Carolina. In preparation for that seminar, I was asked to update a GE publication highlighting fuel flexibility in B, E and F class gas turbines. The culmination of my effort, with help from my close associate Saul, was a technical paper titled "GE Gas Turbine Combustion Flexibility," coded as GER-3946[97]. For the semi-annual SOA conference in Asheville, GE bound all of the presentations, along with a short bio on each author/presenter into a thick Technology Seminar book to be given to all attendees. During the multi-day event, customers were invited to attend selected one-hour presentations on topics of interest. Immediately following the presentations, there were short audience question-and-answer sessions with each paper author. In the evening after dinner, customers and presenters were encouraged to mingle and continue discussions. I really enjoyed these seminars. I could not have been more proud to be working with such a great group of professionals. Certainly I considered it a very high honor to be counted among the chosen to participate in these events.

The Asheville SOA in 1996 was, in some ways, the culmination of all that I had accomplished in Application Engineering. Time was ripe for me to head in a new direction, and I had a keen sense of this. Other GE man-

---

97 GER stands for GE Reference, one of many specialized technical reference documents on a number of topics authored by knowledgeable internal "experts".

agers in the Power business had taken notice of me. One particular GM, a dynamic fellow I'll call EV, approached me and inquired if I would be interested in leading a team for an exciting project he would be overseeing. It seems that the winds of change had again blown my way, so I carefully listened to EV's pitch. As difficult as it would be, I faced the fact that it was now time to move on from what undoubtedly was my most fulfilling and exciting professional role. Building on those experiences, new adventures were just around the corner, but little did I realize how different and challenging they would be.

Chapter 12

GO CONFIGURE!

THE EXCITING PROJECT EV SPOKE of promised to transform our entire front end proposal process. EV's vision involved harnessing the capabilities of artificial intelligence (AI) software to configure, price and describe our complex power products[98]. At the time, EV was working directly for Power Systems Vice President Mark Little and had sold senior leadership on this novel new concept. Powerful rule-based algorithms theoretically offered simplicity, speed and accuracy to what was a specialized, manpower-intensive and complex process. With initial budget approval, along with technical validation from the GE Global Research and IT teams, EV was poised to launch his vision. One missing ingredient was a team project leader to make the vision a reality. As EV pitched his vision to me, noting my years of Application experience, he painted a convincing narrative that I was uniquely qualified to lead the project.

And, I knew, the move was the right one. After all, I had been pondering my "next role" for a while, and the timing was perfect. The position seemed like an obvious extension to leverage my 13-plus years of Applications experience. Finally, an opportunity to lead a team on a major new initiative, something never before tried in our business, seemed appealing. It appeared that all the stars were aligned, and even my internal compass was pointed in the right direction, so I jubilantly accepted EV's offer. I was standing on a precipice of an exciting new role, backed by an enthusiastic executive sponsor with the highest of all possible expectations. What could be better?

With every new job change there often comes a dichotomy of emotions. Gleeful anticipation often is countered by the bittersweet reality of leaving a familiar place you thrived and relished so much. Such was the case here. No doubt I was thrilled to be embarking in a new direction and finally moving

---

98 Our Gas Turbine alone had in excess of 5,000 different equipment configuration options, many of which triggered rule-based needs for additional options. Applications and Requisition engineers were performing this task manually using internal software programs and constantly struggling to keep pace with ever-changing rules on configuration options.

on from my long, fulfilling stay in Applications. On the other hand, I was leaving my comfort zone, not to mention so many long-time trusted associates with whom I had established solid working and personal connections. Frank Brooks, now firmly locked in as Applications Manager, was most disappointed with my decision to leave the team. Further, I think Frank saw that my new project would be in direct competition with Applications' responsibilities, as I would be working to digitize much of his team's functionality. I suppose Frank looked upon me as a bit of a turncoat. That was a negative that I would try to manage in my new position.

EV was a very energetic and dynamic person. Even before I assumed my new role, EV's personal charisma and excitement revved me up. As I assumed the new role, EV already had established a small internal GE IT support team. He had also identified and selected a western US AI software consulting firm to guide our efforts. With this framework in place, I needed to hit the ground running, and quickly hire the remaining specialized team members.

EV's excitement was driving incredible expectations for our new configurator project. Even if they didn't understand AI software, folks across the business who heard of this effort formed their own widely varying interpretations of what exactly a configurator would mean to our business. Expectations ranged from "just another hair-brained idea of the month" at one end of the spectrum to this god-like, all-powerful tool capable of generating an entire power plant proposal with a few mouse clicks. In the midst of this atmosphere, EV informed me we would formally introduce the project at GE Power's annual Global Sales meeting[99], which that year was being held at the Empire State Plaza in nearby Albany, New York.

During the Global Sales meeting, I stood backstage as EV delivered one of the all-time best presentations I ever witnessed. The passion he exuded was absolutely electric as he captivated an estimated crowd of perhaps 600 or more in Albany's Empire State Convention Center. The presentation itself was a masterful collection of simple cartoons and photos without a single word of text on any slide. Undoubtedly, the image-based presentation was a welcome relief to many attendees who had been bombarded by countless overpopulated text and numeric "eye charts" during the multi-day event.

99 The Global Sales meeting was an annual January week-long event GE used to gather hundreds of our world-wide commercial folks together to communicate themes, strategies and generate enthusiasm for the coming year.

EV eloquently vocalized his well-conceived message that impeccably injected meaning to every image on each slide as he marched through his points, and he received a well-deserved standing ovation after concluding his pitch. During the ovation he signaled to our IT manager, and then to me, having us walk out on stage and join him during the extended applause. I'm sure many of my GE colleagues were surprised to learn of my new role. Many in the audience knew me from my Applications days and a good number had directly worked with me. The entire experience was a bit surreal. I certainly felt awkward receiving ovations for a huge task that I had barely started. No pressure here!

My new role was going to continue my education in ways that I couldn't begin to envision. In my humble opinion, with his unbounded exuberance, EV had set expectations unrealistically high. After all, this was a pilot launch using advanced AI software in an extremely complex application. Folks who really didn't understand this endeavor interpreted this as the long-promised answer to all of their frustrations with existing, outdated internal legacy tools. My initial thoughts were that many expectations were completely unwarranted, but I, too, was captivated by EV's passion. Flashbacks to President Kennedy's "man on the moon by the end of this decade" speech popped into my head. Perhaps this idea of setting lofty, seemingly unrealistic expectations was actually a great motivational tool EV was tapping into? Certainly having a charismatic leader like EV was inspirational to us all.

Drawing on my extensive internal GE network, I was able to recruit a super mix of talent to fill out the core team, which nicely complimented the initial "cherry picked" folks EV had already selected. Our IT manager designated a couple of excellent IT experts, who were assigned to the team as well. Next, EV had me contact a recently retired sales executive who I knew from my prior Applications position. I convinced him to hire on as a pensioner consultant to advise our team on commercial issues. Finally, the AI software consultant selected a handful of people to co-locate and work with us.

As we recognized the immense challenge before us, the team came up with a fitting project name of "Merlin" (as in "the great Magician"). The name Merlin conjures up a mysterious, magical force and we all agreed that was an appropriate namesake. Indeed, it was going to take supernatural powers to make this dream a reality. A black-pointed wizard hat, containing stars and a crescent moon, evolved into our team logo.

Now the team and I embarked down what was a very unfamiliar road for most of us. This state-of-the-art coding, known as AI software, was promoted by EV as "Technology Enabled Selling." The tool itself became known as "the Configurator" and was used synonymously and interchangeably with the project name, Merlin. While the word "configurator" may be an unfamiliar term to some, most may be able to identify with one common example. If you have ever attempted to virtually customize or "build" a new car on-line, you were using a version of a configurator. Such codes allow the user to select specific desired features from an intelligent, rule driven pick list of available options that then are compiled to form a customized end product. This is basically what a configurator tool does.

In our case, we were tackling a significantly more complex task by trying to configure power generation equipment for an entire power plant. Here, there were dozens of drop-down pick lists, radio buttons and similar rule-based screen selections. Our gas turbines alone had more than 5,000 configurable options, most of which had interdependencies (defined by prerequisites and rules) related to one or more other selections. Steam turbines and generators added thousands of additional options, making an extremely complex task even more arduous. The "one-to-many" and "many-to-one" interrelationship phenomenon significantly raised the level of difficulty for Merlin. Further, the fact that our products constantly evolved meant that the options, interrelationships and rules governing these features were in a perpetual state of flux. Translation here: The tool would need constant rule updates, testing and frequent new releases to keep pace. In everyone's exuberance at the launch of the program, I don't think many realized the extent of maintenance that would be required, but it was ultimately a key lesson learned along the way.

One additional complication should be mentioned here. Very few people actually fully understood the fact that GE's proposal and order execution efforts were empowered by at least two dozen intertwined legacy programs, some of which were built decades earlier. Even fewer people understood the complex interaction, requiring significant human intervention, to execute projects through this maze of systems.

When we launched Merlin, our business operated on the aforementioned legacy software platforms. While far from optimal, people were reluctant to accept changes to the familiar legacy tools because, despite their quirks, they knew how to babysit these systems to execute their tasks. Folks were reluctant to blindly place their faith in a promised new system because of the tremendous work pressures we all operated to. By hook or by crook these antiquated tools ran our entire inquiry-to-order (ITO) and order-to-remittance (OTR) processes, despite their drawbacks.

EV's vision was ultimately to replace all legacy tools with Merlin. While that was a great long-term goal, we were merely a pilot team launching our initial foray into the AI arena. I often found myself trying to contain the enormous disconnect between EV's ultimate vision and the immediate reality to construct a functional prototype tool. To realistically bound our project, we decided to focus on the mature MS6001B gas turbine and associated 6A6 generator, configured as a simple cycle plant, for our pilot effort. This was a sound and reasonable approach, but I found myself constantly battling scope creep as there was constant pressure to focus on the larger, higher volume 50 Hz (MS9001E and MS9001FA) and 60 Hz (MS7001EA and MS7001FA) products. And of course everybody wanted all of this capability immediately.

The challenges in my new role were many, constantly drawing my attention from one mini-crisis to the next. Some were to be expected and some just totally caught me unawares. Since I had no prior experience in software development, including working through a hired consultant, I was on a steep learning curve. The complexity of the software was making this project even more of a challenge, as it was cutting edge and unlike anything any of us had experience with.

Hosting a software vendor on our campus also complicated things. Software coders, being the resourceful geniuses they are, typically march to a different drummer. I definitely wasn't prepared for the laid-back, non-committal attitudes that, I suppose, are somewhat characteristic of these highly creative folks. On our project, the consultant sent us several very young coders. While they had great technical expertise, their maturity level and business acumen were lacking. To somewhat balance the team, a more experienced leader was assigned to help supervise the younger coders.

The leader himself was a bit of a character. A self-made millionaire, he had founded and then sold his first company and was now firmly entrenched as a partner with this second skyrocketing software firm. But while the younger coders respected their leader, even he had difficulty instilling a sense of urgency in setting and maintaining schedules.

Our consultants had decided they would commute to Schenectady from their far western US base. While I didn't think that was very practical, apparently that point had been agreed upon and included in their contract, so it was not a battle I could hope to win. I will say that the weekly commute was a constant source of aggravation and slowed progress, as the team never arrived before 1 pm on Mondays and always departed by noon on Fridays.

Simply finding office space to co-locate our team was a much bigger challenge than I would have imagined. In the mid-1990's, the historic Schenectady campus was undergoing constant demolition of older buildings to consolidate unused real estate and reduce GE's tax burden. Office space was at a premium, causing managers to closely guard their allocated areas with almost medieval jurisdiction. Somehow EV secured us space in a decrepit office area of long-neglected Building 53. Ironically, this was the very building where I worked as a combustion engineer nearly two decades earlier.

Noting the disarray in our area upon arrival, a few my teammates and I took it upon ourselves to make urgently needed renovations. Risking a union grievance, we unobtrusively came in over a weekend, personal power tools in hand, and re-arranged partitions, hung white boards, moved desks and created a conference room. All of this was just to make the place functional.

Concurrent in time to my leadership of the Merlin team, Jack Welch was busy inflicting his influence on the company as well. Welch had become enamored by a statistical tool known as Six Sigma[100]. The tool had yielded phenomenal results improving manufacturing applications, so now it was being applied to all facets of our business, including commercial transactions. Welch extrapolated the concept by making a grandiose decision to impose Six Sigma usage in every corner of GE, in the hopes of driving the company to even loftier heights.

I can easily write an entire chapter on this bizarre initiative, but instead I've opted to provide only a few minimal comments. For those who want to read more about misapplied episodes of this endeavor, please refer to my footnote below[101].

---

100 This disciplined, statistical-based, data-driven approach and continuous improvement methodology is designed to eliminate defects in a product, process or service.

101 Former GE employee Mary Kuykendall's book "Rebuilding the GE House that Jack Blew Down" is available via Amazon. I personally know many of the characters mentioned and I experienced much of what she discusses.

Many of my colleagues viewed Six Sigma as an ill-conceived initiative, however they simply went along for fear of reprisals. In some applications, particularly in commercial areas, the implementation was quite draconian, often leaving individuals struggling to comply with dictated objectives. Many in GE's skilled workforce were quite clever. They wisely leveraged Six Sigma requirements into objectives that were needed anyway. Unfortunately, others simply "invented" useless projects merely to superficially fulfil program requirements. I couldn't possibly estimate the immense hours and dollars expended on so many of these wasted efforts. Of course, the target metrics always were made to indicate "improvements", usually at the expense of broader business impacts, no one even considered.

As a motivational enticement, key individuals were selected to become "Black Belts" or leaders to help coach and ultimately approve or reject required Six Sigma projects. Those who completed Black Belt requirements were "promised" a faster road to promotion. I turned down such offers as my heart wasn't behind the program. Perhaps that decision was career limiting, but I stand by it. Meanwhile, I observed many who moved along this "fast track" only to end up in ill-suited positions, eventually leaving the company or being forced into less desirable positions.

Tackling the daily management issues, technical problems, personnel, budget and schedule were not my only concerns. While all of these kept me fully engaged and scrambling, there was a much bigger issue that arose barely a month into our effort. Without warning or any explanation, EV suddenly disappeared from his office. Days became weeks and weeks became a month and then two months, with absolutely no word. Rumor and speculation were running rampant. Was he sick? A family issue? No one knew. Certainly this was a major distraction for all of us involved.

Bad thoughts crept into my head, and rumors kept flying on what was really going on. Then one day, out of the blue, I, along with each of EV's direct reports, received notice that EV would return the following day for a 9 a.m. staff meeting. I was thankful that we would finally be getting past this mysterious absence and its associated effect on the team's morale. Unfortunately, the explanation and ramifications were beyond what any of us had imagined.

Honestly, I don't ever think I've attended a more shocking staff meeting in my entire career. As promised, EV did appear and opened the meeting with a stunning revelation: He was leaving GE, effective at noon! All of us at that meeting were flabbergasted by this disclosure. About the only other information EV would share was that he had discussions with our CEO and decided he could no longer work at GE. Therefore, he was "leaving to pursue other opportunities," which most of us understood as the politically correct phrasing surrounding something negative that was not to be discussed publicly.

EV's decision was quite an emotional letdown both for me and the team. My team was one of two major groups, along with several direct reports, that EV was managing. I had absolutely no idea what was to come next, but certainly this was a most unexpected situation. For the third time in my career, my hiring manager had suddenly departed within the first few months of a new assignment. Experience in the previous episodes was not good, and this announcement, too, felt quite ominous. Still, this was an uncontrollable event, and no amount of whining or worry would positively change the outcome. I simply had to deal with it.

Shortly after EV's startling announcement, I was called in to meet with EV's manager, Vice President, Mark Little. I had met Mark briefly on a number of prior occasions so, while not totally familiar with one another, we certainly were not complete strangers.

As I recall, my meeting with Mark was quite cordial and direct. Basically, Mark advised me that EV's team was being split into two groups, each to be led by a manager reporting directly to himself. Next, he offered me a choice of either accepting the role of manager of the Configurator team or become acting manager until a permanent one was chosen, and I immediately accepted the manager position. Mark promptly stood up, reached across the desk, and shook my hand to consummate my decision. As of that moment, Mark said he would be making a substantial compensation adjustment commensurate with my new position. In the excitement of the moment, I did manage to thank Mark, and I may have said something to the effect that I thought my first decision appeared to be a good one. Suddenly I was now an official GE manager, with direct reports and all the associated responsibilities.

As I left Mark's office, many thoughts ran through my head. I could hardly believe that I was now on the staff of one of the most senior vice presidents in Schenectady. Adjustments were going to be made. I needed to pull an executive level briefing together, so Mark could better understood our team and progress. A new cadence for meetings would need to be established. I wondered how the team would react to this latest development. In any case, my immediate duty was to gather the team together and inform them about this latest development. Our team would certainly be getting even closer scrutiny and now, through me, had a direct link to our most senior leadership.

I recognized that Mark was a very busy senior executive. Although I now had a direct channel to such a high-level executive, I needed to act responsibly to manage the team in a manner fitting with the trust Mark had placed in me. I clearly understood that there were many more important issues on Mark's plate, so I would need to minimize any disruption or distractions to him. Mark always was quite cordial to me, and I intended to work diligently to manage this team to make him proud.

As part of my new staff role, I now was required to attend Mark's 7 a.m. Monday staff meetings. My presence at those meetings was a huge education for me. Witnessing first-hand the issues and strategy discussions as well as observing the styles of other managers, including Mark's response to each, was an invaluable experience. No doubt being part of a GE senior staff was certainly one of the high points of my privileged career.

I'll say right now that working for Mark was a wonderful experience that I am most grateful for. Even though I put great pressure upon myself and often stressed over preparations for each face-to-face meeting, Mark was always a professional and a gentleman in his interactions with me—and I certainly can't say that about every GE executive that I met and interacted with. Mark is at the very top of the list of great GE leaders that I worked for.

Eventually our team delivered a prototype MS6000 gas turbine generator plant configurator. During the rollout demonstration, we received plenty of feedback from across the business. The breadth and scope of the project actually pushed the limits of our company-issued personal computers just to execute the AI software. Yes it was huge, complicated and sometimes ran a bit slow, but it certainly demonstrated such a tool could work.

The team even figured out how to automatically generate a proposal Electrical One-Line diagram and Mechanical Outline drawing, as well as descriptive proposal text write-ups for the plant, something no other single tool had accomplished. But our successful prototype only led to even more requests to add more products, features and capabilities. At some point there would be a decision to either invest significantly more resources into the program or move in another direction.

During the three years I led the team, we delivered some impressive modules. Our deliverables generated enough promise each year that we were funded and allowed to continue working, although progress never seemed fast enough for anyone. As modules were completed, some were used in creating actual proposals, but Merlin never did become the tool EV and others had initially envisioned. The reality of constant maintenance, new version releases, and slow PCs trying to execute the massive code was just too much to overcome.

Ultimately, the answer was to bring the tool up to a higher level of configuration detail where weekly product perturbations would not be so impactful. Dialing back Merlin's focus to a higher configuration level made the code more useful for faster, accurate, and more comprehensive budgetary estimates. The higher level budgetary Merlin solved a number of nagging issues, like shrinking the code footprint, allowing for faster processing on available laptops, and eliminating the need for weekly updates. It also afforded time to build in additional product capability. GE field representatives now could generate a complete budgetary quotation in a few keystrokes. The quotations included specific high-level proposal text, Electrical One-Line and Mechanical Outline drawings, plus budgetary pricing tied to a specific scope of supply[102]. In essence, a specific budgetary quotation, including a customized letter, could be generated from Merlin within 24 hours anywhere around the globe. Not such a bad compromise[103].

As we all contemplated this new iteration of Merlin, destiny again intervened and changed my course. As the new millennium approached, market conditions for power generation equipment had changed rapidly. Deregulation opened up the merchant power markets in the US. Availability and abundance of natural gas fuel, combined with deregulation, helped launch an historic, dynamic growth bubble for combined cycle (gas-fired combustion turbine and steam) power plants. At the forefront of this bubble were several

---

102 To maintain consistency across global regions and customers, a manual HQ approval review was established as part of the process.

103 Even after 20 years of technology advancement in computer software, hardware, and cloud computing, plus many more millions of dollars spent, GE never was able to develop a comprehensive power plant configuration tool as envisioned in the late 1990s by the time of my retirement in 2016.

of GE's largest utility customers. One such customer, with whom I had much prior experience, was poised to become a mega player in this upcoming explosion of new merchant plants. Little did I know that this customer still remembered me and was about to make a startling request for my services.

Behind the scenes, this Southeastern customer made inquiries through our commercial team about my availability to work with them on a newly launched mega deal. A fellow, I'll call TM, a previous associate, now commercial director for North America, approached me to assess my interest. While I was curious about TM's inquiry, I had no idea where the discussion was leading. Quickly, TM laid out the situation and straight out asked if I would be interested to be the GE lead customer contact on a multi-year mega deal with this customer.

What an unexpected and flattering surprise! For one of our most strategic customers to make such a special request for my services was an incredible honor. Adding even further esteem was the fact that GE management considered me suitable to fulfill the function. Undoubtedly this was a very unique and unusual circumstance, and in my heart I knew almost immediately that this new position was for me. I quickly affirmed my interest as TM and I continued to talk through the details.

A few days later at a lunch meeting with JS[104], our GM, the discussion culminated with a plan to create a first-of-a-kind position called Strategic Customer Manager and appoint me into the role. Concurrent with the official announcement, I promoted my technical leader from the Merlin team, into my prior manager role. Just like that, I was entering the new millennium in dramatic style.

---

104 At this point, I was also fortuitously reporting to JS, after he had petitioned for and was granted direct control of the Configurator project from Mark Little.

Chapter 13

WHALE ENCORE

IN STARK CONTRAST TO PREVIOUS dire statements from senior GE corporate leaders a decade earlier, the US power market stormed back with robustness never believed possible in the industry. Availability of relatively low-cost, clean-burning natural gas, low electricity reserve margins, growing power demands and industry deregulation, plus other market factors, unleashed unprecedented demand for gas-fired power plants.

In response to the market opportunity at hand, a major GE customer formed a merchant segment of its business, separate from its traditional regulated core, to more swiftly develop new plants across the country. Installation speed was the name of the game as developers raced to capture lucrative cyclical spark spreads[105]. This customer alone would end up constructing 30 new plants, literally from Maine to California, during this unparalleled "bubble" of new gas-fired combined cycle power plants.

In the newly created role of Strategic Customer Manager, there really wasn't time for traditional training on this assignment. Not that I was uncomfortable with that. I knew the customer and their culture. Combined with my solid technical background, extensive internal contacts, and willingness to adapt and learn, I felt very confident. Basically, my job was to launch each new project, assuring that all equipment was released to Manufacturing and Sourcing according to our customer's schedule. While that's a simple one sentence summary, there were literally thousands of details to be addressed along the way. Once again, I would call upon my many contacts, knowledge of how GE operated, and my own personal experience to address whatever issues arose. And believe me, there were issues.

On the GE side, I was reunited with my buddy BB, who still was in the role of account executive for this dynamic customer. BB and I had been through

---

105 Spark spread is the difference between price of electricity received by generators and the cost of fuel to produce that electricity. During the bubble years (approximately 2000-2003), developers could recoup the cost of a new plant in just a few peak months due to the demand driven surging prices of electricity.

many battles on the original "whale" project, so we both were pleased to be working together again on this much larger encore performance. It's always good to have a proven anchor point when the going gets tough.

On the customer side, there was a single familiar person, a fellow named Paul, who had been the man responsible for bringing my name up in the first place. I really respected Paul as a knowledgeable, honest, but demanding individual. As difficult as it was to satisfy him at times, I admired his thoroughness and tenacity to drive for the best possible deliverables from GE. When I thanked him for speaking so favorably of me, ultimately leading to my appointment, he advised me not to be so quick to thank him, as serious difficulties lay ahead. While I brushed off his comment at the time, assuming it was meant in jest, I soon learned there was a more subtle message in his words. Within the first months of my assignment, Paul suddenly announced he was leaving, as he refused to relocate to Texas as his company requested. His faith, family and friends came first, and Paul wasn't about to let work disrupt his priorities. While I was most disappointed, I acknowledged and respected his decision. Still, I found it remarkable that Paul had been involved just long enough to advocate for me in my new assignment before departing. You just can't script events like this.

So, the first order of business was to meet with the customer team, who happened to travel to Schenectady in my very first week on the job. Upon learning of my appointment, their management likewise designated a counterpart position to essentially mimic my function in their organization. At this meeting, I met my counterpart, Daniel Barpal, along with his key associates. Since Daniel and I had never met before, I suppose we each were a bit wary of the other. Both of us were newly hired into our current positions, so naturally we would be learning and defining our respective positions simultaneously. It would take some months for Daniel and me to get to know each other, but somehow we ended up bonding quite well. There was much at stake for each of us, so it's good that we were able to quickly establish and maintain an excellent professional relationship.

Probably no position I held in my career was more thrilling than that of Strategic Customer Manager. For starters, I would imagine that few people ever get embroiled in managing billion-dollar contracts. While I worked as part of a very skilled team, I played a decisive role in executing these projects. Without doubt, there was plenty of opportunity for a major snafu that could have derailed progress and reflected badly on both companies. Luckily, Daniel and I worked extremely well together. We both stepped in to handle hot issues as they arose while always keeping our personal emotions in check. Between us, we hammered out acceptable compromises that averted countless larger confrontations.

One continuously challenging issue was that circumstances required the concurrent parallel development of multiple plant locations prior to each project release. At the latest possible moment the customer would decide which site was the next most lucrative location. Every site had its own set of unique challenges, thereby impacting site readiness for construction to commence. Air permitting, soil, environmental variations, local codes, specific fuel compositions, noise levels and the like were variables that triggered configuration changes in our equipment. Remember all those thousands of options I talked about in the previous chapter? Site construction schedules, transportation routes, along with GE's ability to manufacture equipment in our full-to-capacity factories further complicated each decision. At the end of the day, Daniel and I had to agree and coordinate on final equipment configuration, shipment/delivery dates, and countless other details for each individual project before I could "release" the equipment. By release, I mean that I was responsible for getting signoff from senior leadership to commit our manufacturing and requisition teams to begin executing. This formal "release process" required all our GE internal teams to approve scope definition and schedule. I literally interacted with dozens of GE folks, in multiple locations, for each project launch. Daniel was running a similar gauntlet on the customer side. The pace was fierce, and it didn't change for three successive years.

My unique background in Applications, especially in air permitting, drew me into helping the customer obtain some contested permits at a number of sites. I even engaged my long-time former colleague, Marv Schorr, who was now retired, but still doing selective consulting, to help out a couple of times. Once again, Marv and I were reunited, traveling together to educate regulators as we assisted our customer to obtain timely project permits. Personally, I found this unique aspect of my job especially rewarding and worthwhile. No doubt this was a win-win for all parties.

GE assigned a terrific team of project managers to execute the bubble projects under these contracts. I'll digress for a moment here to mention that three of our four dedicated strategic project managers were former military officers, and they were just super to work with. GE picked up on a great recruiting notion when it began recruiting former military officers. Known as the Junior Officer Leadership Program (or JOLP for short), the program was quite successful in bringing aboard some really awesome individuals, and it was a true privilege for me to work alongside these guys and gals.

I even ended up with an important assistant, who was actually an Annapolis graduate who also came to us via the JOLP program. BW was instrumental in helping to update our contracts and track finances across each project. Like all of the JOLPs I worked with, BW was a very loyal, competent and hard-working partner. Periodically we had to modify or extend our customer contracts, which led to long multiday meetings. When we held these meetings at our Schenectady Headquarters Customer Conference Center in Building 37, I took every step to make these encounters as efficient as possible. Since I was hosting one of our most highly valued customers, I was always given priority for the best rooms in the facility. Our meals were catered with top quality foods, and the level of service we received on site was exemplary. As good hosts we could do just about anything to make the meetings efficient and make our guests feel welcome. More than once Daniel, BW, myself and all associates on both teams, consumed all three daily meals in that conference center during these marathon negotiating sessions. Without a doubt these were very demanding times, but in the end I know everyone felt good about what we accomplished.

Daniel and I were routinely in daily contact (via email, phone, text and even, on occasion, fax) but given the magnitude, duration and complexity of our business, we agreed that periodic face-to-face meetings were still needed. We did our best to minimize travel expense by varying meeting locations between Schenectady, Greenville, and the customer's Texas offices. Over the span of years, people came and left the teams, so Daniel and I felt it necessary to maintain solid relationships that can only come from in-person meetings.

My Strategic Customer Manager role was exciting. On any given day I interacted with perhaps 20 or more folks, from Manufacturing, Engineering, Logistics, Sourcing, Project Management, Finance and Services. Many of these people were located in different states, and in some cases different countries. For instance, our Schenectady generator and steam turbine factory was at maximum capacity, so we decided to source some generators from an approved supplier in the UK. Keeping tabs on these activities was critical to maintaining project cadence, so Daniel and I were locked at the hip as we orchestrated power plant projects spanning the entire continental US.

Being so intensely focused, there was not much time to reflect on the magnitude of what we were doing. Looking back now, I hope this period in GE's Power Generation saga will be remembered for the amazing and historic period that it was. As we approached three years into the "bubble" it occurred to us that we were nearing an unprecedented milestone of the 100th shipped turbine to this customer. GE was determined to mark this occasion with a day-long celebration at our Greenville facility. The idea caught on, and I was thrilled to play a central role, working closely with GE's Marketing Communications people, who pulled out all the stops to direct this massive event, including guided plant tours, professional photography, press coverage and exquisite catering.

All customer and GE senior executives, along with primary contributors from both organizations, were invited to participate. Both local and state government representatives as well as local news media also were welcomed. The event was about the most extravagant I can ever recall in my entire career.

After struggling to come up with a suitable memento, I suggested a laser-etched crystal paperweight to mark the occasion. A continental US map, marked with stars indicating locations of each customer plant, was determined to be a meaningful memento for the design. I found a vendor, in Israel of all places, to create 50 of these crystals. After placing the order, a bit of unwanted drama arose as tensions flared in the Middle East, delaying shipment of the crystals. In an extraordinary twist of luck, the crystals arrived by priority delivery in the nick of time.

In preparation of this milestone celebration, Daniel and I spent many hours tracking down aerial photographs of each plant site, which I inserted into an annotated Power Point Slide show. The Marketing folks added background music to the show, which alternated between actual site photos and the US map display indicating the geographic location of each plant. During the luncheon, the impressive slide show was featured on a giant screen, creating an inspiring backdrop for all to appreciate.

Under the backdrop of cloudless Greenville skies, a locomotive towed an MS7001FA, representing the 100[106]{th} shipped unit, just outside of the manufacturing building in preparation for a massive group photo opportunity. Perhaps a hundred of us posed in front of the massive 7FA unit for the giant group shot.

After the plant tours concluded, Daniel and his senior leaders passed a note to me and my manager requesting that we all meet for dinner that evening at a local establishment. While we were surprised by this request, Daniel and his team indicated a sense of urgency, so of course we obliged. TM and I were somewhat concerned by this unplanned dinner request. Our concerns would be born out in just a couple of short hours.

As I sat at dinner with this mix of GE and customer leaders, the mood should have been celebratory, but instead there was a palatable negative vibe in the air. Over cocktails, our customer passed out a confidential document with the ominous title "Scorched Earth Scenario." In a striking irony, on the very evening of our massive day-long celebration of the 100th turbine shipment, our customer was announcing to us that the historic bubble was about to burst.

After three spectacular years, the unprecedented explosion of turbine orders was ending. Sure, there were a couple of dozen units still in the pipeline, but that was going to be it. While GE had negotiated strong cancellation clauses in our contracts, our most strategic customer now appealed for special consideration as the power markets had peaked and a downturn in spark spreads was apparent, negating the need for additional plants.

As expected, our leaders came to an "understanding" regarding the termination of contracts. Daniel and I worked through the details as we executed remaining projects still in the pipeline. In a most peculiar twist, GE was asked for advice on "deconstructing" a couple of plants so they could be more easily "mothballed." Several of my associates were dumbfounded as I pressed for responses to this bizarre request. Unquestionably, this assignment created some very unusual work situations.

As things wound down on my Strategic Customer Management adventure, my thoughts again shifted to the future. What would come next? Many of us were thinking the same thing. Would this chain of events lead to more

---

106 In actuality, the utility ultimately purchased a total of 136 units (44 7FAs and 72 7EAs, along with 22 D11 steam turbines) during the bubble in the 1999-2003 time frame.

layoffs? That had been GE's standard operating procedure in the past. My commercial assistant BW and I discussed this, but I repeatedly assured him things would be fine, even though I didn't have any idea what would actually happen.

With the ominous cloud of uncertainty hanging over all of us, we all kept plugging away at closing out all of the work-in-progress. Working under the constant pressure of the bubble projects, I certainly appreciated all of my co-workers who were not only super professionals, but also very congenial personally. I especially became good personal friends with my close associate BW, drawn closer in part due to our common aviation interests. BW was a Navy helicopter pilot, so he had plenty of stories to share with me. My modest aviation experiences paled compared to his. Yet we both enjoyed talking of flying and I actually helped BW joining a local flying club.

By his nature, BW was always extremely punctual. Whenever he was delayed or ran into unforeseen scheduling conflicts he always notified me. One morning, when I noticed it was past 10 a.m. and I still hadn't heard from him I was quite concerned. I reached out and spoke to a couple of his fellow JOLP's to ask if anyone had been in contact with him. Several of them, including BW, had been "celebrating" late into the prior night. One of the party guys had just left work, heading over to BW's apartment to check on him. Little did I realize we were all about to experience one of the saddest and shocking events of my entire career.

Later that morning, my manager TM called an impromptu meeting of our small team in his office where he relayed the most stunning and awful news I could imagine. Earlier that morning, BW had returned to his apartment, apparently distraught and depressed, and shot himself. The news was so traumatizing that I really don't remember much else after that, except repeatedly asking myself "why?" No one had any answers, nor did we have any idea what to do next.

Human Resources arranged for counselors to meet and speak with us, so I suppose that was a start. In these situations, there are always so many questions and so few answers. My manager and others who had been with BW that final night met with local authorities as the family was contacted. Several of us went to BW's apartment to clean up in anticipation of the arrival of his two older sisters. BW had often spoken to me about his two young adult sisters, but I could never have envisioned meeting them under worse circumstances. We all hugged and cried together, all searching for answers, but there just weren't any.

Days later, our company covered the costs for a select group of BW's closest associates to travel to a funeral service in Maryland—a very sad, difficult and gut-wrenching day. Out of respect for all, further details of this horrific event will remain private.

BW's sudden and unexpected death further exacerbated the negativity I was feeling as the great sales bubble came to an end. As I look back on this period, I certainly remember all of the great accomplishments achieved during the extraordinary US turbine bubble, perhaps the greatest such period in GE's history, but I also remember my close associate and loyal friend BW, his life tragically cut short by an event none of us can really understand. I hope you have found peace, my friend.

My training and education were always technical. Dealing with the death of a co-worker, particularly suicide, is just not a topic I was prepared for. Occurrences such as suicide, which thankfully are relatively rare, are simply not expected to happen. When they do occur, we are caught unaware and are completely floored by such happenings. I wish there were some way I and others could have been more aware of the situation so such a tragedy could have been averted.

A few months later, I was approached about another position in the Commercial Operations segment. Once again, a position was discussed that could be customized toward my skillset. While there were some appealing aspects to the position, the move would involve a leap of faith as I didn't have strong personal connections to the manager. However, by this point in my career, I was open to seek new opportunities. One aspect of the position that was particularly appealing was the opportunity to mentor younger, high potential technical sales trainees. In any case, I pushed aside my apprehension by focusing on the positives. It was a plus that I already knew several others already in the group. Perhaps I lulled myself into a false sense of security, but with no better options in sight, I accepted the new offer.

On my very last day as Strategic Customer Manager, I received a phone call from a customer Vice President. While I didn't have a great deal of contact with the gentleman, I certainly knew him from his participation on my weekly teleconferences and in numerous meetings we both attended.

Although our interactions were limited to emails or short commentary on conference calls, he had been keeping a closer eye on my activities than I realized. On this day, he called simply to acknowledge my work over the past three years. He told me that I had very positively and significantly contributed to the overall success of many projects. What sticks in my mind was that he perceptively noted that GE probably would likely never fully recognize the importance of the contributions I made, but he wanted me to know he recognized my impact and he personally thanked me for my efforts. He followed up this personal call with a very thoughtful, though less directly worded "attaboy" email message. Really a classy guy!

Hearing such glowing remarks from a high-level customer executive was very astonishing and meaningful to me. Somehow this man had attuned himself to the fact, that despite my center stage position, I labored mostly behind the scenes with minimal acknowledgement. His call to me on that day was the most impactful and complimentary recognition that I ever received from a GE customer. My work had been appreciated by the most important judge of all, our end customer.

I didn't have any idea what lay ahead, but that uplifting call erased any sense of melancholy and put me in a very positive mood, despite the anticlimax as I concluded one of the most significant and successful assignments of my entire career. No matter what awaited in my next role, I would be launching into it on a high note.

Chapter 14

ANALYZE THIS!

IN HINDSIGHT, IT WAS A BAD DECISION. I probably should have thought through some longer-range career planning before accepting the new position. Instead, I let the fact that I genuinely liked and trusted most of the people around me lull me into a false sense of security.

Things started out just f.ine as another customized position and title was created called Analyst and Training Manager. The group, was a functional mix of pre-bid support, analytics and pricing which had evolved over many years. Included on this team were gas turbine, steam turbine and combined cycle experts who focused their efforts on developing early pre-bid studies, economic analysis and performance estimates, for GE equipment. Still others worked on estimating competitive market pricing analysis for each new unit bid. All in all, it was a pretty autonomous, self-regulated group populated with mostly senior folks who had been in their respective positions for many years.

Another important function served by this group was providing required rotational training assignments for new Technical Sales Program (TSP) participants. All trainees were required to do a minimum four to six-month assignment in the group. I was assigned as the Training Manager during the rotation, responsible to make sure the two to three trainees under my watch were progressing satisfactorily through the various skill sets they need to master while on this assignment. Part of my job was to help address questions, suggest remedial actions and generally manage them through any issues or conflicts that arose. I also was required to provide regular feedback, as well as to complete a written evaluation for each trainee at the end of his or her assignment.

The new group pretty much ran itself as the manager, a career GE guy, was primarily focused on managing upward. I'll call him BF, and he had established himself as a guru for all things involving power equipment pricing. Routinely he was called into senior-level private meetings with our GM and/or VP to offer his insights on new orders. The market had become much more competitive after the gas fired plant "bubble" burst, so the business of power generation equipment returned to its dogfighting ways. GE was using every possible advantage when bidding each order and "Prof. BF", as he liked to call himself, had everyone convinced that his input was most crucial.

My primary focus was always on the trainees, and I made sure they each received every bit of attention they deserved. One of my trainees, a young fellow from Taiwan named Simon, was exceptionally sharp. I helped guide him through a couple of cultural issues, including one where he almost lost his international driver's license. Possessing a rare combination of technical ability, curiosity and interpersonal skills that separated him from his peers, Simon continually amazed me with his business acumen and poise well beyond his years. Once, he hosted a couple of the other trainees and me at his apartment for a home-cooked Taiwanese meal he prepared. This guy was on track to do very well in GE, and he earned my highest performance ratings of any trainee I supervised. It's not surprising that he went on to enjoy rapid advancement within GE. Since Simon always keeps in contact with me, I do know that he went on to become one of the top Sales people for GE's Aviation business in the Asian market where he ultimately was assigned. Simon, I'm really glad to have known you, and watching your continued success makes me very proud.

A new challenge for me in this assignment was taking on more complex project economic analyses. This entailed learning new tools and the subtleties associated with these analytics, and I gained a new appreciation for business metrics I had never considered. My peers had worked these tools for years, but I was only now gaining some competence with them. I worked to fit in developing these new skills within an already full agenda of other responsibilities.

During this assignment, I was still representing GE on the International Gas Turbine Institutes' (IGTI) Electric Power Committee, which helped me maintain my connection with broader industry issues. Leveraging my gas turbine air emissions background, I co-authored an ASME/IGTI technical paper on startup and shutdown air emissions and personally presented the paper at the Turbo-Expo conference in Atlanta, GA in June 2003. My colleagues and I had recognized that misconceptions among customers and regulators alike had, in our opinion, incorrectly focused on volumetric pollutant measurements during gas turbine startup and shutdown. Our paper helped drive focus toward total exhaust pollutant measurements on a mass basis, which is a more meaningful reference. Volumetric pollutant levels change so rapidly, along with exhaust flows during transient startup and shutdown operations that attempts to measure such wildly changing numbers provide little useful information to either quantify or ultimately control emissions. Our paper seemed to be well accepted, and we used it to help drive regulators toward adopting more sensible legislation, measurement and validation.

The IGTI committee took advantage of my GE role and approached me to ask our VP, Mark Little, if he would accept the honor of becoming the keynote speaker at the Turbo-Expo 2003 conference as Atlanta was a GE headquarters city. It was customary for the keynote speaker to be a business executive from a company with a strong local presence. When I approached Mark with this request, he accepted on the condition that I handle all interface details. Of course I accepted this condition knowing full well the increased workload that went along with my acceptance. The added workload seemed a small price to pay for the benefit of assisting a senior executive prepare himself for such an address and I was not disappointed by yet another unique experience.

Meanwhile, at the request of my manager, I was asked to pull together a short course on "cost of electricity" analysis, which I had just studied in detail myself alongside the trainees. I did so, and taught the course several times in Schenectady, plus several more times across the globe via our virtual computer conferencing network. I really enjoyed teaching and got plenty of accolades from the folks I interacted with.

I most definitely relished working with the local GE "field guys," many of whom I had previously encountered in my Applications days. Reconnecting with old colleagues was mutually beneficial and was always enjoyable. Usually I received a question or two about gas turbines, and I welcomed the opportunity to continue helping old colleagues address their most recent customer questions and issues.

After completing a year in this group, it was time for our annual performance review. Literally out of nowhere, with no prior mention of any performance shortfalls, I was flagged as a Least Effective (LE) employee. Talk about being ambushed! This entire LE thing was a carryover from Jack Welch, who arbitrarily set a threshold that every group should annually identify their "least effective" folks. Once "identified," those in this category were intended to be placed on a Performance Improvement Program (PIP) to either improve themselves or ultimately to be forced out of the company.

Over the years I had seen many of my colleagues, put in this unsettling and usually undeserved predicament. Some groups rotated various members who took turns being the LE person, just to fulfill this ridiculous arbitrary quota. Time and again I had seen this edict misapplied, especially in groups where each member was a highly trained, experienced expert that would never be considered "least effective." Whenever I encountered such nonsense, I always worked with folks to get them through what usually was a bogus improvement program. Now, I had been blindsided and put in the very position I had helped many others overcome.

Words simply are not adequate to describe my dismay. Somehow in a year I had gone from managing what was arguably our most important customer, involving billion-dollar contracts, to being least effective? What was wrong with this picture? Given the road that I had traveled, with more than 30 years of GE professional experience, resulting in so many accolades and awards, this unfair review was completely inconceivable. If my departure from this team was the goal, and it appeared to be so, things could have been handled in a much more considerate manner. Instead, a management decision was employed that caused undue anxiety and hard feelings.

Upon regaining some composure, a couple of days later, I re-read what my manager had written in the appraisal. As I pondered his words, it struck me that nothing he wrote was particularly negative. While there were glaring omissions of my milestone accomplishments, I was mystified that his written comments just didn't seem to support an LE rating. Based on this assessment, I carefully crafted a non-emotional, fact-based written rebuttal. My written commentary was one of the most potent documents I had ever written, and I wondered what response it would elicit. To my surprise, there was no response whatsoever. No one—not HR, not my manager, nor his manager—ever responded to my rebuttal. What discussion, if any, took place at all, I'll never know, but no feedback ever reached my ears.

As I look back on this experience I believe the real problem was not at all performance related. Rather, I suspect a combination of personalities, misunderstandings, prejudice and mismanagement motivated the review. Although this was a most unfortunate and painful episode, it was in no way unique in GE. My only reason to even recount this event is to point out that life can be unfair, and inevitably things will go awry at some point. It is during these challenging times that our character and resilience are tested the most. What really defines who we are is how we respond. My response took every bit of determination and fortitude I could muster.

Certainly, having a great support network helped immensely. Each time I faced difficult times, I was very grateful for the support I received. Whenever I encounter someone else going through similar difficulties, I'm reminded of my own hard times. I feel it's incumbent upon those of us who have been helped to "pay it forward."

In this case I once again reached out to my network of GE colleagues to plan my next move. Clearly I needed to find a new position, but I understood the difficulties in making such transitions given my situation. Somehow in my heart I believed there had to be a way and, sure enough, another opportunity materialized in very short order.

This time my life boat took the form of a long-time co-worker by the name of Harold Miller. Harold was managing a Conceptual Design[107] group that, by coincidence, happened to have an opening for an engineer. I contacted Harold, who knew me and my capabilities well from my Applications days. After a brief discussion, during which I outlined the situation, Harold assured me he would assist in getting me to join his group. I shall always be grateful to Harold, for stepping up to help a fellow in need.

My move to Harold's Conceptual Design group signaled my return to Turbine Engineering after a nearly seven-year hiatus in the commercial world. Amazingly, the transfer happened within about a month or so from that underhanded review. In perhaps what served as a fitting lack of conclusion, no one ever mentioned anything about a Performance Improvement Program (PIP), nor was I ever placed on such a program. The whole situation was so bizarre and ridiculous that HR didn't even bother to follow its

---

107 Conceptual Design was a forward looking team advising the business on competition, disruptive technologies and advanced concepts for next-generation equipment, among other things.

own procedures, which of course were not warranted. I simply assumed my role as a senior engineer on Harold's team, immediately plunging into a new initiative as if nothing had ever happened. Fine by me. Little did I know where this position would lead, but I had a new lease on my career after another trying experience.

Life on Harold's team was good. Harold was an intelligent, strategic thinking engineering manager who had the respect of subordinates, peers and senior leadership alike. Beyond that, he was simply a good, decent man, husband and father. I couldn't ask to be working for a better individual in the entire Power business. Fate had once again corrected a wrong and landed me in the perfect place.

On the Conceptual Design team, I was reunited with several former colleagues, including Dwayne McDuffie. Dwayne was easily the most knowledgeable person I knew when it came to our turbine performance Cycle Decks. Since my Combustion days, I had solicited help from him and was never disappointed. Here again, he was instrumental in catching me up on the latest Deck upgrades made during my absence from Engineering.

I was assigned to support a new after-market program targeting performance improvement concepts for our large 7FA installed fleet. I found myself spending long hours on teleconferences collaborating with our Greenville colleagues. The program had several names, but ultimately the final deliverable product became known as Cooling Optimization Package (COP). The name stems from a series of secondary cooling air[108] reduction modifications resulting in significant performance improvements. Since there already was a large installed base of both 50 Hz and 60 Hz FA products, the after-market opportunity was very lucrative if we could deliver on these improvements.

Prior programs suffered from a series of over-commitments and underdelivering on promised improvements. Harold had warned me about this, so I was especially determined not to get caught up in the hype and politics often associated with these programs. My estimates would always be fact-

---

108 In gas turbine speak, primary air is the air entering the compressor that actually travels through the combustor to mix and burn with fuel. A smaller portion of the total air is known as secondary air or secondary flow, which bypasses the combustor and is used to cool various hot gas path parts. Secondary air is loss to the system, so minimizing this amount of secondary flows improves performance.

based. If there were shortcomings, I would report them and make alternative suggestions. No way would I "stretch" the numbers just to meet some ill-founded expectations.

Possibly my approach rubbed some folks the wrong way. However, in the end we delivered solid turbine modification packages that could be confidently guaranteed to deliver the expected performance improvements. It was really gratifying to see these after-market products evolve and deliver solid results for the business.

Time marched on and Harold ultimately retired from the group, which opened new questions on who the next manager would be. Given that the Gas Turbine Engineering center of gravity was now in Greenville, a new fellow based there took over the group. He came north to visit team members, announcing he would be making some changes. Working for a manager you hardly know, who is located 800 miles away, can never be an easy thing. So the handwriting again was on the wall; it was time to search for a new position--again.

Hoping my proactive searching could avert another potentially unfavorable situation, I, along with others on the team, began investigating new opportunities. Unexpectedly I was approached by an up and coming leader I'll call CG. It seems CG was forming a new team called Integrated Performance. CG recruited me to join the group in a special new role he titled, Performance Quotation Process Leader, to help drive new improvements to our gas turbine performance and associated risk calculations. As I read the formal job description, it seemed this position was ideally suited to both my background and experience. Without hesitation, I accepted CG's invitation and was appointed to the new position.

During my first year, CG proved to be a super guy to work for, and we made great progress. I even was reunited with my longtime colleague and informal mentor Berkley Davis, now in the newly established role of Chief Systems Engineer. Berkley was a key driver as I took on a major task to re-write our internal Design Practice guide for Gas Turbine Performance. Everyone involved with gas turbine performance estimations or guarantees needed to comply with this guideline. I was engaged for nearly a year in what turned out to be a controversial, sometimes outright contentious effort, as both commercial and technical folks had strong viewpoints about how we determined and presented performance guarantees. In the end, I completed a rigorous review process and obtained all the required approvals. My extensive prior commercial knowledge—experience very few of my technical colleagues possessed—was certainly an advantage that served me well in this effort. Completing this task was a major personal accomplishment, and the opportunity to again work closely with Berkley added to my satisfaction.

CG quickly nominated me for promotion to the title of Principal Engineer[109]. When my nomination was approved, I joined an elite group alongside some of the best engineering talent in our business. It certainly was gratifying to attain this level of recognition, and I'm very grateful to CG for promoting me.

Experiencing this success in my career was amazing. Sometimes it felt almost too good to be true, especially considering how I had been side-tracked by an undeserved review only a few short years back. But an old nemesis that had haunted my GE career from the very start was about to intervene and once again create further havoc following my latest success. With little forewarning, CG was tapped by the business into a new role. Just like that, after only about a year into my assignment, the person with whom I had established a terrific rapport, who hired and promoted me, was suddenly gone.

For six months following CG's departure, there was a power vacuum on the team. These situations never are good, and it didn't take long to go from bad to worse. Inexplicably a young and inexperienced person I'll call TT, based in Greenville, initially was named acting manager. Rumor has it that more experienced candidates had turned down the position, but one can never be sure about these stories. Having failed to find a suitable permanent replacement for CG, our Engineering leadership decided to make TT the permanent manager. Neither I, nor any of my senior colleagues in Schenectady, were at all happy with this situation.

TT appeared one day in Schenectady to introduce himself and meet with all of us in what our HR folks like to call "new manager assimilation." From the very beginning, TT introduced some strange ideas and changed much of what CG had set up. He seemed especially focused on modifying my role and didn't seem at all comfortable with me. However, I had amassed

109 Not long into the new millennia the Engineering vice president established an alternative career path for technical experts who choose not to follow standard managerial career tracks. Principal, Consulting and Chief Engineer roles requiring GM and/or VP approval were created.

an impressive resume of solid accomplishments, so despite his displeasure with my activities, TT was hard pressed to find fault with my work.

During my tenure with Integrated Performance, leadership was pushing the senior folks to be creative, especially in the area of patentable ideas, otherwise known as Intellectual Property (IP). Hoping to influence some younger colleagues, I teamed with selected associates as we submitted, and ultimately were awarded, several new patents. It had been nearly 30 years since my first GE patent. Now a handful of additional patents were assigned to GE in my name and the names of my co-inventors. While the number and magnitude of my patents may not be all that notable, it still enthralled me to be forever included in this inventive fraternity, following in the footsteps of Edison himself.

Meanwhile, I still was dealing with TT, who continued his troublesome redirection of my responsibilities as defined by CG. In what seemed to be an attempt at harassment, TT appointed me Quality Representative for the Schenectady team. He did so knowing most folks despised these roles, because at this point, people began recognizing the fallacy behind many of the quality efforts associated with the often misapplied Six Sigma initiative. Still, now that GE had obtained ISO 9000[110] certification, regular on-going audits were required to maintain accreditation. While I was initially quite annoyed by this assignment, I became even more determined to thwart TT's latest attempt to badger me.

Disenchanted folks sometimes referred to GE's Six Sigma program as "Sick Sigma" because of the aforementioned ill-conceived projects aimed at improving specific metrics, often causing negative ripples in other ignored areas. Irresponsible individuals made outrageous claims and manipulated data backing their declarations. At the end of the day, however, quality re-work costs to the business betrayed the illusion. So many mischaracterized, make-work projects were performed employing dubious metrics for justification that folks cringed whenever a quality program person showed up at their desk. I had to overcome this stigma when I became the group Quality Representative.

---

110 ISO stands for International Standards Organization (actually a Swiss-based federation known as International Organization for Standardization). It represents about 100 countries. ISO 9000 is a series of quality systems that define, in generic terms, how to establish, document and maintain an effective quality system.

As I would come to understand, ISO 9000 was, in fact, a sensible and rational guideline for implementing, documenting and monitoring an effective quality program. Group quality representatives were encouraged to become ISO 9000-certified auditors, so I took advantage of this and enrolled in a week-long course. After passing a comprehensive verbal and written exam, I became a certified internal auditor, earning accolades from the course instructor. As required, instructors passed along written evaluations on each attendee to managers. I can just imagine TT's reaction as he read about my latest achievement.

Armed with an auditor's perspective, I set up sensible ISO 9000-compliant practices to assure our team benefited from proper quality procedures. Over the next several months, I received positive responses from teammates who recognized and appreciated my rationale. Suddenly, our prior red and yellow metrics changed to green, indicating successful compliance with the processes we implemented. Several on our team also passed internal audits given by outside auditors[111].

As time for annual appraisals arrived, I fully expected TT to hammer my review based on our sharp disagreements. While he wasn't that blatant, he did nail me by minimizing my compensation as he glossed over my accomplishments. Minimal salary adjustments late in one's career are not a pleasant experience, as pension calculations are based on highest salary averages. When I challenged TT on his reasoning, he offered little in the form of an explanation, but clearly he was motivating me to leave or quit. The winds of change were whipped up once again. Little did I realize my next opportunity would launch me on the most spectacular culmination of my career that I ever could have imagined.

---

111 As an auditor, I was not allowed to audit my own team for obvious conflict reasons.

Chapter 15

COMPLETING THE CIRCUIT

AGAIN REACHING OUT TO MY now well-established network, I began another quest for a new position. Steve Hartman, a General Manager with GE Power's Services Engineering group, was high on my list. Steve and I met sometime in the early 1990s at various ASME/IGTI Power conferences. At the time, Steve worked for Strategic Power Systems (SPS) [112], owned by that company's CEO and founder, another former GE colleague and longtime friend, Sal DellaVilla[113]. Sal hired Steve directly out of college as a reliability engineer. During those years, Steve often accompanied Sal to conferences, to assist with busy schedules, giving us all an ideal opportunity to interact both personally and professionally. Eventually, in an effort to broaden his career, Steve left SPS to join GE. Over time, Steve steadily worked his way up the leadership chain to a services General Manager position.

The power and timing of a single phone call is remarkable. Right off, I learned Services Engineering was on the verge of launching a new initiative called Total Plant Services (TPS)[114]. Experienced engineers were definitely needed to help in this effort. Following an exchange of a few more details, we concluded the call with positive anticipation of a mutually beneficial solution.

Not long after my conversation, another manager, JM who worked for Steve, contacted me. After a brief discussion, JM set up a personal meeting with me for the following week, when he planned to be in Schenectady. Our appointment was, in fact, an informal interview, and it went quite well.

---

112 Strategic Power Systems is a well-known turbine industry company that helps customers monitor, understand and improve reliability and availability by monitoring, analyzing and acting upon real-time data generated from their operational assets. SPS also benchmarks customer data across participating industry fleets using data from virtually all major OEMs in the Power Generation business.

113 DellaVilla and I served together on the IGTI Electric Power Committee for decades.

114 TPS was GE's initial launch into complete plant services offerings that treated the entire plant as a system of inter-related assets.

While I'm sure Steve had briefed JM about me, I'm glad JM took the time for a face-to-face meeting to better assess for himself if I was a good fit.

Soon after my meeting with JM, a formal offer was extended for me to join the team as a staff principal engineer. Just like that, my struggles with TT were over. But more importantly, I was being launched into a wonderful new set of circumstances that would propel my career to a spectacular conclusion that I would never have thought possible.

Immediately after accepting the new role, I was pleased to learn that another former Schenectady GE colleague, EC, who had recently relocated to Atlanta, had also just been hired by JM. Together JM, EC and I, were the cornerstones for the new Engineering organization within TPO, as we set out to identify additional candidates to staff remaining team positions.

While most of JM's team under Steve was to be based in Atlanta, I made it clear that I was committed to remain in Schenectady for personal reasons. Given the ubiquitous internet, conference lines and other virtual connections, remote work was now a widely accepted practice throughout the company, so my situation presented no problem whatsoever. As it turned out, my Schenectady location actually resulted in a fortuitous upside that was one of several unexpected positive twists that contributed to my unbelievably fabulous series of late-career experiences.

Leveraging my locale, JM and Steve asked me to be the liaison to GE Global Research (GRC), located nearby in the town of Niskayuna[115]. Power Services had provided considerable funding for services-related work at GRC, so it was beneficial to have a locally based person to follow these efforts. In this role, I became familiar with various services-related programs while monitoring progress, addressing questions, and generally advocating for our business priorities. It was hard to imagine a more enjoyable assignment than working with cutting-edge technologies in a world-class laboratory setting. Little did I realize things were going to get even better.

Call it fate, or some other supernatural force, but whatever it was there was something just completely otherworldly about my good fortune in returning to Services. In a very literal sense, I was returning to the business segment where I first began, which although unplanned, actually brought my career full circle.

115 The GRC in Niskayuna was the headquarters of GE Global Research which, at the time, had branches in a number of global locations. The Niskayuna campus encompassed over 500 acres, housing laboratories in many technical disciplines.

Becoming the liaison to GRC was a godsend. I say this because the assignment allowed me to meet a new and dynamic person at GRC who would be a tremendously positive influence on me for the remainder of my career and beyond. That person was the GRC Power Services Technology Leader, Russell "Rusty" Irving.

Rusty was a senior executive at GRC. As a senior leader who came up through the GRC ranks, he had extensive knowledge, contacts and insights to virtually every major program at the center. I don't think I could over-state how terrific he was to work with. Just a single phone call or email from him would quickly accomplish in hours things which would require days or weeks for mere mortals. In yet another coincidence, Rusty reported to my former boss who was at that time GE's Chief Technology Officer and leader of GRC, Mark Little.

From the moment we met, Rusty and I seemed to be totally harmonized. Somehow, destiny brought us together, and it would be quite difficult to single out another individual in my career who was more enjoyable to work with. As we got to know each other better, it was absolutely mind boggling how closely we were aligned on so many levels; even our personal interests were in parallel. Sometimes just as I mentioned a notion, Rusty would say he had been think-ing nearly identical thoughts. I liked to call it "mind-melding".

To help better launch the TPS initiative, Rusty suggested that Steve and JM consider conducting what was known as a Session T (for Technology) at GRC. While such events could take many forms, Rusty envisioned a two-day working meeting in Niskayuna where select Services personnel would interact with relevant lab technologists, to plan, collaborate and prioritize a roadmap forward. Such events require significant amounts of pre-planning and home-work by all to ensure a successful outcome on a compressed schedule. Choos-ing the right individuals and managing the total number of participants were critical to a successful session. JM and Steve liked the idea so, given my loca-tion, I partnered with Rusty on the pre-planning to help make this happen. While it was quite an effort, it was also a super learning experience for me and the teams. I literally had a front row seat, assisting Rusty with organizational logistics while also being an active participant for the event. The session also afforded me the opportunity to meet many of my Atlanta-based teammates, as well as various GRC technologists working our projects.

An interesting concept gained traction from our Session T activities. Since the "voice of the customer" was deemed of highest significance, I suggested that we consider collaborating with one or two local area power plants operating GE equipment as an ultimate advanced prototype validation facility. If we could develop a mutually agreeable working arrangement, the plants offered a convenient test bed to validate advanced prototype hardware or software. Over the next year, after considerable involvement with legal teams from both organizations, Rusty and I were able to sign a test agreement with one of the local plants.

During my tenure, we executed a handful of experimental hardware installations at this plant, two of which paved the way for new product offerings for the after-market team. In addition, our relationship with the plant was such that Rusty and I arranged for select GRC personnel, associated with the experiments, to visit and tour the plant. Surprisingly, a number of the GRC folks, actively engaged in power technology development, had never visited an actual power plant before! While there is no concrete way to measure the benefit of these trips, I have to believe we made a tremendous difference by introducing these talented theorists to the "real world."

My affiliation with Rusty and the GRC teams was a most wonderful experience filled with interesting people, technologies and just plain fun. One memorable area that Rusty introduced me to was robotics. GRC was heavily engaged in cutting-edge robotics research and development, so when Power Services expressed interest in tapping into this area, I was elated to gain exposure to this very interesting technology. I suspect my fascination with robotics stems back to my early childhood science fiction interests, where every TV show or movie seemed to have a robot character.

When the robotics team shared its latest work on unmanned aerial vehicles (UAVs), my mind was launched into hyper drive as any talk of flight always peaks my interest. One afternoon I invited my long-time GE colleague, Rich Loud, now a fellow Principal Engineer, to participate in a drone demo. Like me, Rich is an avid aviation enthusiast who also happens to be a top-notch radio control aircraft pilot. As I had presumed, we both had a terrific experience. In the following days after our visit, Rich and I had some follow-on discussions. Why couldn't we use a UAV to make power plant measurements, particularly in Rich's area of expertise, acoustics? Our discussion led us to jointly file for yet another patent, which has since been granted. It's simply incredible how one fun-filled afternoon could generate such a useful idea that may one day significantly improve the way we make acoustic measurements at power plants.

On one of his Schenectady visits, JM invited me to join him at a major meeting of a global team developing the next-generation advanced HA (high efficiency, air-cooled) turbine. This new class of turbines was considered critical to our future position in the gas-fired combined cycle power generation market. Development of a new turbine line is a major, long-term business commitment involving significant investment of funding and technical resources. Accordingly, our business assigned its top talent to work this critical program.

During the multi-day review, JM and I came up to speed on progress made by the team thus far. Along the way we discovered the HA team desperately required input from Services, so JM immediately committed that he and I would support this need. In that subtle commitment, fate was once again intervening in my career.

My involvement with the HA program, particularly with the launch of the very first 9HA project in Bouchain, France, quickly evolved into a full-time commitment as I essentially became the Services point contact for the HA program. Ironically, the TPS business initiative modified its priorities, affording me the time to execute this role shift. Joining the elite HA team was a high honor as I was aligned alongside many of the best engineers in our business. Where have I mentioned that before? It's simply amazing how my career seemed to gravitate me toward the most talented folks in our business.

Organizational changes were also taking place to align with changing business needs. The net result was that I ended up as a direct report on Steve Hartman's staff. Even more impressive was that Steve himself was made a company officer and promoted to Services Engineering Vice President. As far as I know, I had suddenly become the only Principal Engineer in GE Energy[116] who reported directly to such a senior leader. I'll always be grateful that Steve welcomed and maintained me as a direct report for the final years of my career. More importantly, I have to salute Steve for giving me the autonomy to use my own judgement in making and implementing key decisions. As a result, I

---

116 Business name changes regularly took place. GE's Power business was called GE Energy during this period.

drove timely and appropriate allocation of resources assuring that Services was well positioned to meet the needs of the HA product line.

The HA product was truly a multinational development effort. While I knew many on the Schenectady-based team, I had to quickly assimilate with perhaps a hundred other global team members spread across the US and half a dozen European countries. When I say global, I really mean it! Meeting European contacts often required "cold calls" to personally introduce myself and establish connections. When the need for more direct interactions became evident, I arranged and chaired multi-day Work-Out sessions[117] in Atlanta, which was a reasonably convenient gathering point for the geographically dispersed teams. At the Work-Outs, I arranged for various design engineering teams to present product design details and features to European Services personnel, soliciting inputs from the latter. Although much of the design was already complete, there were still a number of areas where Services feedback could still be incorporated. Certainly, the meetings sensitized Product Engineering to start thinking about improved serviceability as part of design criteria. In hindsight, we should have engaged the Field Services team much sooner. Early involvement would have instilled even more serviceability attributes into the design from the very start. Still, we made some tremendous progress, and in the end improved the product. Take note all you future product developers: Think about servicing your product in the earliest design phases.

Following the first Work-Out, it became clear additional structured communication was needed, so I instituted and chaired weekly Services teleconferences with cross-functional participation from European and US-based personnel. Thanks to the cooperation of many participants on these calls, the agendas always generated lively and helpful discussions. I then published careful notes and distributed these to all participants, encouraging affected groups to take follow-up actions. These conference calls seemed to take on a life of their own as we established a solid rapport between teams separated by the Atlantic, ultimately obtaining closure on countless issues.

The teleconferences uncovered a services tooling issue that seriously lagged hardware design. New, specialized tooling would be needed to as-

---

117 The two sessions were held about a year apart, with the latter building upon results from the initial meeting, plus the weekly follow-on teleconferences that became part of my routine.

semble and disassemble new components for both initial factory assembly and later for maintenance outages. Further, a scheduled full load test would need to be conducted ahead of first unit shipment, so that exacerbated the tight timeline. The launch single-shaft HA product not only had a new gas turbine, but the generator and steam turbine were also new products, which further magnified the tooling impact. Specialized tooling requires considerable investment capital, along with skilled people, for development and validation, so the challenges were significant as we played catch-up on this issue.

Because of the tooling situation, I quickly aligned with a relatively new Greenville-based team known as Outage Engineering (OE). The OE team had been created to improve maintenance across the product lines, but had prime responsibility for developing new tooling. I began a close and rewarding involvement with these people, who impressed me with their skills, dedication and spirit. Literally everyone I worked with in OE put forth tremendous efforts in pressure-packed situations. While we were always under the gun, this team was as resilient and resourceful as any I have ever been associated with.

I also must give credit to some really super and talented co-workers for their amazing contributions. Included here were my new Europe-based Services associates and those at the Global Tooling Centers, who made multiple trans-oceanic trips in support of our efforts. These folks provided Herculean efforts to meet near impossible timelines. Let me add my personal thank you right here and now to all. You were just spectacular to work with, and I'll forever be grateful for your cooperation, loyalty and inspiration. It's hard to put into words how thrilled and privileged I was to work with you.

Criticality dictated that we used some unorthodox methods to short circuit GE bureaucracy. And, because I was on Steve Hartman's staff, I was able to get us the attention we needed to break through bureaucratic roadblocks.

One perplexing problem involved moving a one-million-pound generator, aligned between the gas and steam turbine in our single-shaft design, for what we hoped would be very infrequent rotor servicing. The problem led us to seek out help from a specialized lifting vendor. As the Services point contact, I spearheaded an effort involving a world-class UK-based heavy lift company, which I can state is easily the finest most professional vendor I ever worked with. The vendor helped us develop a novel servicing solution using jacks and beams to lift and laterally translate the generator for rotor access. Multiple patents resulted from our efforts, adding to my growing number of GE patents. In the final year, prior to my retirement, we successfully validated the concept and associated hardware at the Bouchain, France site. It was absolutely a brilliant effort, and I want to acknowledge the dozens of folks who were involved with this amazing project, which showcased teamwork at its very best!

Speaking of patents, my Services work during the final years of my career led to a plethora of patents. Previously, I had been granted about a handful of patents, but in my last few years, there was an explosion of patentable ideas that I and my co-inventors filed. As of this writing, 17 patents have actually been granted to me and my co-inventors by the US Patent Office, not counting those filed in a few select foreign countries. Several others still remain somewhere in the patent review process. Although 17 isn't an overwhelming number, for a simple Schenectady kid, I'm just astounded that I was able to achieve this. What is even more astonishing is the fact that GE has actually built and will be using some of these ideas going forward. What would my grandparents think now?

As if all of this was not enough, as I was moving toward the end of my career there were even more good things happening. As my close colleague Sean O'meara and I were attending a video conference in celebration of Engineers' week in February 2015, we suddenly saw our names and photos appear on the large overhead screen, along with those of several other colleagues, denoting that we had won a business award for our HA work the previous year. Sean and I stared at each other, jaws wide open. As further punctuation for our efforts, nearly the exact same scenario occurred again in 2016, as we were again designated as business award winners, a mere three months before my retirement. Talk about going out on a high note!

There is yet one final experience, as I was working toward the end of my career, that couldn't have been more fitting. As readers may remember from Chapter 1, the reason I became so transfixed by science and technology was the US Space program. I closely followed NASA's progress on the manned space missions as it worked to fulfill President Kennedy's vision to put a man on the moon. Naturally, my heroes were the astronauts who were the public faces of Mercury, Gemini and Apollo programs as I grew up in the 1960's. My love for space, technology and flight never left me.

So, when I learned that a retired Shuttle astronaut was coming to speak locally at Proctor's GE Theater[118], I purchased a last-minute ticket to the event. As fate would have it, I somehow landed the last front row seat for what turned out to be one of those life-altering experiences. During the approximately two-hour event I, like others in the audience, was mesmerized by a fellow named Dr. Story Musgrave[119].

Actually, I learned, Musgrave, was far more than just one of NASA's most experienced astronauts. He is one extraordinary human being, who just happened to be an astronaut who had flown on all six US space shuttles. Perhaps his most notable mission was leading a repair team to correct optics and other problems on the Hubble space telescope. In any case, everyone attending was treated to an enlightening evening that delineated Musgrave's remarkable life story. After the talk, I immediately joined the queue for a brief meet and greet. Here I obtained, a most cherished photo alongside a man I idolized. Little did I realize this was only the beginning of my involvement with Story Musgrave.

Days later, while still feeling inspired by Musgrave's talk, I sent him an email expressing my gratitude and thanks for his poignant presentation. To my surprise, he personally responded to me, and that was the start of a truly epic series of encounters with this unique individual.

As a pilot, Musgrave had flown thousands of hours on aircraft powered by GE engines, so he had great respect for these turbines and the company that built them. Noting my technology background and GE affiliation, Musgrave expressed interest in possibly doing a future speaking engagement. Of course, I knew I had to find a way to make this happen.

My first action was to approach my now-close associate Rusty Irving at GRC. While a bit skeptical at first, after some of his own investigation and a conference call I arranged between Musgrave, Rusty and myself, the gears began to turn. Rusty soon became as enthused as I was about this incredible person and the possibility of meeting him in both small group and larger audience settings.

---

118 GE Theater is a flexible, 434-seat, black box-style theater used for intimate single performer shows or other smaller events. It is located adjacent to Schenectady's landmark and historic Proctor's theater, a fully renovated 1920s vaudeville-era playhouse that hosts a wide variety of modern performing arts.

119 For more details on this amazing American, please see his website: www.storymusgrave.com

Fast forward a bit after I had arranged funding for Musgrave's visit courtesy of GRC and the local American Society of Mechanical Engineers chapter. Musgrave's visit took on a life of its own as I worked out the busy two-day itinerary. The stage was now set for me to personally escort one of the most inspirational characters I ever met. Over the next 48 hours, from arrival to departure, I was Musgrave's personal guide and chauffeur, and I took advantage of this rare opportunity to spend extended time with a this fascinating man who happened to be a personal icon. Included were some very informal small group private meals and one-on-one talks with a truly exceptional human being.

The ever thoughtful and resourceful Rusty arranged accommodation at GRC's executive lodge for the two-day visit. The later logistic allowed for even more invaluable personal time with our most esteemed guest. All in all, it was a whirlwind two days, with events ranging from small meetings to a public lecture at Schenectady's Museum of Industry and Science, culminating with a masterful presentation at GRC entitled "Design A Life for Yourself – One Little Step at a Time." The GRC event has to be considered one of the best ever held in that venue. I say that not because of the laser-like attentiveness of the audience, nor the long rousing standing ovation Musgrave received. Either of these would be impressive in their own right, considering the caliber of scientists and engineers at GE's premier research lab. What sticks in my mind is that months after this talk, when walking GRC hallways, people would come up to Rusty and me, thanking us for arranging that inspirational talk. Speaking for myself, I was filled with elation and a genuine sense of fulfillment for playing such a pivotal role that had inspired so many people.

Any words I might use here to convey my feelings about the days I was able to spend with a man who embodied everything I had ever dreamed about regarding space would be woefully inadequate. My experience was surreal on many levels. The hours I spent just in quiet one-on-one discussions or over meals defy description. His recounting of various Shuttle flights, space walks, piloting other jet aircraft, parachuting, gliding etc. were simply phenomenal. I believe the word that best captures a description of Dr. Story Musgrave is polymath—someone who is extraordinarily learned and at the same time highly skilled in very broad subject areas. When one considers his modest start growing up on a farm in Stockbridge, Massachusetts, with terrible tragedies punctuating much of his life, you have to marvel at the man. He embodies a rare combination of technology and an appreciation of the arts. Very humble and giving on many levels, he was a joy to be around, and I'm so grateful to have gotten to know him on such a personal level. Story Musgrave is probably the person most like my favorite historical figure, Leonardo da Vinci, that I will ever meet. Once again, I was privileged that my affiliation with GE made it all possible.

Almost a year later, I again hosted Musgrave, this time at both GRC and GE's main campus in downtown Schenectady with help from my long-time friend Berkley Davis and another chief engineer, Meng-Ling Hsiao. On this visit, we held deeper discussions in smaller group settings at both locations, along with a larger audience presentation at our main downtown auditorium. For the large group presentation, it was a tremendous honor for me to introduce my iconic hero, and now good friend. Once again, the presentation had the desired effect of inspiring the audience. Who could ever imagine that that first grader who became hooked on the space and technology in 1961 would befriend and host one of NASA's most experienced astronauts all these years later?

In the final year of my career, GE was completing a long-time purchase of former European rival Alstom. The acquisition, the largest in GE's history, was a long and complicated affair, closely followed by the media. Negotiations with the European Union and various other governmental entities certainly added complexities. In the end, GE was faced with a massive integration issue, spanning almost a dozen countries, new products and a host of cultural difficulties. In the immediate aftermath, timing and poor performance seemed to hinder success of the integration. It is unclear how this will ultimately pan out.

As I was winding down my activities in preparation for my anticipated retirement, my manager, Steve Hartman, asked me to work closely and report to a former Alstom Vice President named Christian Verhoeven, who had now joined the staff. I must say that I enjoyed meeting and working with Christian for what was really a short few months. Timing just doesn't necessarily always work out. Somehow, I feel shortchanged, as I know I would have enjoyed a much more extensive working opportunity with Christian.

Again, I sensed one of those pre-destined bonds because we shared some very similar interests and background experiences. It definitely was my pleasure and, yes, I'll use the word again, privilege to work with Christian, even if the time was brief. He is a very knowledgeable, witty and interesting individual, who I know is capable of doing great things for GE. Steve definitely ended up with a super person to join his staff.

In my last months with GE, as I approached my 40th work anniversary, the company presented an incentive package to ease the financial transition into retirement, so I accepted the offer. In the final days before my retirement, I arranged one additional visit by my friend Dr. Story Musgrave. This time Musgrave visited and spoke to the Gas Turbine Engineering community at GE's massive Greenville, South Carolina plant. While I did not make the Greenville trip, my career-long colleague Berkley Davis, along with Chief Engineer Meng-Ling Hsiao, traveled from Schenectady to host our guest. Based on direct feedback, I learned that once again Story Musgrave delivered big time. I just couldn't have been more pleased to help in orchestrating yet another terrific Musgrave presentation to so many.

On May 1, 2016, I officially began my retirement and collected the first of what I hope are many GE pension checks. For the record, the May 1st date was 16 days shy of my official 40th professional anniversary date. In any case, I spent the better part of five decades with GE. As I walked out the door the final time as a GE employee, I was filled with gratitude and certainly felt privileged for all that I had experienced. I was and am grateful certainly for the things I learned, for the amazing challenges that came my way, for all of the many places that I got to visit and most of all for the outstanding people I got to meet, work with, learn from and can call my friends. Regressing for a moment to the Prologue of this book, I hope I did my grandparents proud.

EPILOGUE

Since my retirement, the headlines from GE have been mostly negative as the stock price has dropped substantially and a litany of problems have surfaced. There is certainly no shortage of finger pointing with themes like greed, poor business decisions, lack of oversight and a puppet board of directors all appearing in various media. Despite the negative publicity and accompanying abysmal financial performance, GE arguably still produces some of the best aircraft engines and industrial gas turbines on the planet. This outstanding achievement, despite turmoil stemming from senior corporate leadership, is no coincidence, but rather is a resounding vote of confidence for my outstanding associates who continue to execute their jobs with competence and professionalism.

Given all the recent negative publicity surrounding GE, I didn't want to end this book on a gloomy note. Instead, I decided conclude with my personal farewell message, sent out during my final week, along with many of the upbeat, heartfelt and sometimes humorous responses I received in reply. It's my way of returning gratitude and thanks to all who wrote and so many more who didn't. I love you all, and apparently there were some mutual feelings out there as well.

Final Farewell Message – Reflecting on 40 years at GE

Dear GE Colleagues & Friends,

I want to take this opportunity to leave a parting message that captures some of my perspectives and feelings as I prepare to embark on my retirement adventures next week (4/29). It has certainly been my privilege to work alongside so many diverse, talented and interesting people for these past 40 years. My career has been nothing short of extraordinary. In a fitting and unusual twist of fate, I'm ending my career where it began, with a Services Engineering team, so in this sense I have come full circle.

During my career I traveled extensively and represented GE on four continents in about 20 countries and 40 states. I chaired an ASME/IGTI Electric

Power sub-committee for 23 years, which afforded opportunities to interact with so many global industry peers and experience being a panel speaker, paper presenter and session chair/co-chair at many worldwide technical conferences. My assignments involved extensive customer interactions, especially in Application Engineering roles, particularly in the US with major Southeast US utility customers as I helped GE win major orders with each of these strategic customers. The air permit testimony I provided for these, and many other customers, in more than a dozen US states, not only helped our customers obtain permits, but more importantly helped regulators better understand our equipment and capabilities so they could adopt more meaningful legislation. Along the way, one of the most enjoyable assignments I had was to participate in "live" State-of-the-Art presentations along with other key GE "experts" across the USA. Certainly, I never realized I would enjoy such interactions so much despite the challenges and pressures that were always present in each of these events.

A key reality at GE, and also in life, is change. My GE career was a microcosm of broader life changes. Seven US presidents held office during my career (Ford, Carter, Reagan, GHW Bush, Clinton, GW Bush, and Obama). During this time I worked under three markedly different GE CEOs—Reggie Jones, Jack Welch and currently Jeff Immelt. I personally had 28 different managers in my career, including two VPs and six GMs, including one who is also now a VP. I directly interviewed and was hired into only by about a handful of these roles, while all others occurred through attrition, unexpected promotions or re-organizations.

Probably no period in GE history experienced more turbulent times or enormous technological and productivity transformations than that which occurred during my tenure from the mid-1970s through today. The extensive GE Power business downsizing in the 1980s, particularly at the Schenectady plant, was a reflection of changing economics, company restructuring, a very polarizing CEO and several other influences. Computers and the internet totally re-defined how we work and tremendously impacted individual productivity, leading to countless changes that are still on-going today and no doubt will continue to accelerate in the years ahead as GE moves on with current digital initiatives.

My career was a continuous learning experience. Everyday dealings with so many skilled, culturally diverse and knowledgeable people impacted me in many different ways. Nothing could have prepared me for the wide range of professional and personal experiences that were a part of a career spanning five decades. Without a doubt some of the folks I worked with are the best people on this planet in their specific fields, and it was absolutely my privilege to work with and learn from every one. Each of you inspired me and drove me to accomplishments I would never have thought possible. I owe a huge debt of gratitude to so many colleagues who contributed to my development along the way. Many of you are not only GE co-workers, but also have evolved into solid personal friendships that I look forward to continuing for many years to come. To that end, I'd like to invite all of you to continue to stay in touch—at least via email or one of the other social media now available (Email—PRIVATE), LinkedIn, or possibly Facebook, which I use very minimally).

Some of you have asked what I plan to do with "all that spare time." While I can't envision any "spare time," here's a couple of things on my to-do list: First, I hope to "pay back" a bit by volunteering with local groups and also by providing some career talks/counseling to younger folks to help encourage STEM careers. Also, seemingly endless home maintenance/remodeling tasks await. Some of you in the Schenectady area may also see me on one of the many local bike paths—particularly along the Mohawk—or in the local GE fitness center. I plan to be based in the Schenectady area and, even if that changes one day, I will always have a presence here (particularly in summer and fall). Certainly I plan to visit 10 remaining states that I've not yet experienced, plus hopefully a few new international destinations. Finally, I plan to write a book about my GE experiences, again to help influence some STEM careers for younger folks. Writing a book will truly be a very challenging project, but my GE experiences were incredibly unique and I think will make interesting reading, which I hope will inspire a new generation of talent. I have some awesome folks lined up to help with this task, including my very special retired NASA astronaut friend, Dr. Story Musgrave.

Thanks again to all of you as I'm wishing each of you continued success as you move forward in your careers advancing technology and improving our world every day!

Best,

Mike

Below are most of the actual email responses I received to the above message:

I was moved by your message below. You will likely find, as you suggest, that rather than a life of leisure, your retirement represents a significant change in your life to the next level of new and exciting activities. It has been my honor to work with you, and I especially enjoyed our association on the seminars we presented to regulatory agencies throughout our great country. You represented GE in a most favorable manner, always knowledgeable, professional and articulate, and you always helped to make our trips enjoyable.

I hope that we can continue to meet for lunch and on other occasions.

May your end-of-the-month retirement be the start of a long and enjoyable phase of your life. You deserve it.

My best regards to you.

Marv S.

Mike,

It has certainly been a pleasure & I'm very excited for you for this new chapter, especially looking forward to seeing your book on the NY Times Bestseller list!

I definitely want a signed copy—let me know when your launched book signing will be!

;-)

You've certainly been afforded many opportunities, & I'm sure what you've included in your parting words of wisdom are certainly but a drop in the bucket for all you've seen, done, experienced over your impressive career with GE.

All the best with your many projects & thanks for all you have done to support me & the various teams over the past years!

Best Regards,

Carl M.

Wow! You must have started with the company when you were 4 years old!

Seriously though, I'd just like to say a huge "Thanks" for all your help on the plant NPI programs we've been doing over the past few years, getting the maintenance access etc. design in was a major break-through that'll have benefits for years and years to come and what was equally great was the seamless fashion in which you worked with the NPI design folks. Steve Hartman commented to me a while back it was one of the best collaborative efforts he'd seen and he mentioned it in an all-hands session here in Greenville.

While I missed the session when Story (Musgrave) came to Greenville I watched the video of it in complete awe of the man and what he's accomplished so, you have indeed got a very special friend there. I even showed my kids.

I wish you a long, happy and fulfilling retirement.

Thanks again and all the best,

    Iain K.

Congratulations - about time!

Matt has been keeping me up on your progress. Glad you made the big decision. Also glad to see you have a full plate in retirement—it's the best thing.

I was especially interested in your plans to write a book. I have just completed a local history book called "War on the Middleline," which will be published by LULU circa August. I've been working on it for about 2 years, just now ready to send it to the publisher.

Maybe you, I and Matt can get together sometime to share stories.

Good Luck!

    Jim R.

Although no battle plan survives the first contact with the enemy, one has to have a plan. You have a plan and will do well. All the best in the future.

    Harold M.

Just read about your retirement...that's great! It was a pleasure working with and learning from you. And thank you for bringing me into the EPC. Hopefully our adventures with the [our] projects will make a blurb in your book and if I can assist with anything let me know. And if you make it to Denver/CO, please let me know.

    Daniel B.

Hi Mike,

I wish you the very best for your retirement! CC'ing my personal email address, though I think we're already connected on Linkedin. Also I want to *tell you thank you for all the support and encouragement that you have given me, and I hope that one day I'll have a retirement note that looks a little like yours below.*

Sandra K.

Well Congrats...finally. You will find this episode in life very rewarding as you get into the swing of things. The hardest part is being your own boss and pushing yourself past the "I'll do it tomorrow, I'm retired" phase.

We haven't been able to get to lunch lately due to my adventures in house buying in Atlanta. We actually closed on a house You can see what it looks like on Trulia the address is ..... There are several pics of the place on this site.

We are heading back to GA this Thursday, and then on to Houston to visit my third son and welcome his second baby into the world. We will be there till the first week in June, back up north around the second week in June. I will definitely try lunch then. You really ought to try lunch with Tom E and those guys. Bob Gessner, Dick A., Darwin Brudos, Bill Rowen, Fred Wilhelm and other show up on a regular basis. I think you will enjoy it.

Have you heard from Mike R? Is he flying his WACO yet?

Talk soon, hopefully not by pocket dialing.

Frank B.

Congratulations and Best Wishes are in order from the EPC as a whole to a distinguished and well recognized member of our committee as he begins a new period in his life – that member is Mike Davi.

Mike, you have well earned this new opportunity and adventure. When you complete your book you will continue to influence the industry. You will attract the young and the old to a career opportunity through knowledge and commitment... just as you did!

Sal DV

Mike, congratulations on this and I echo the wish for blue skies and tailwinds. It's been great working with you when we did and also knowing you were doing what you do. All the best in retirement.

Genghis K.

Another very little fact ... Mike Davi put me in for my first GE Power Award! (Support on Merlin)

Thanks again!

-Bob M.

My best wishes go with you...

May you have days full of laughter and happiness...

And may you have a lifetime full of love and dreams achieved—I will remember you although it was a short time from the time we met (heard) until the day you now will leave. You have left your indelible mark,

We will miss your professional expertise and knowledge and wish you only success and happiness in your future endeavors—may they be all that you hoped for!

Cornelia "Conny" B.

It's been a pleasure to work with you. You were always a good sounding board and ally for some of our crazy ideas. Good luck in retirement and have fun. If you are ever in the south give me a call. I'll give you a call next time I'm in Albany and we can grab dinner.

Tom M.

Very nice write up. I appreciate the wisdom and understanding that you brought to your job, and our interactions, particularly in my early GE career.

Best of luck with your very interesting plans!

Bill G.

I was surprised to see your retirement e-mail being circulated, but glad I did.

You were always one of the people I admired and looked up to. One of the reasons I am where am I now is because of you. You were an impressive representative of the teams you were on and the main reason why I wanted to get into Applications, which has now evolved into me being on the current Sales team. Thanks for that!

To keep this short, I wish you a VERY long and happy retirement. You will be missed! Hopefully our paths will cross again.

Best of luck.

Bernie T.

Mike – congrats on the retirement......... I trust you are happy about it.......
Was always a pleasure working with you and will continue to carry the ASME/IGTI mantel...........enjoy your free time.....and hope to see you around.

Andy D.

Congratulations and best wishes for a long and exciting retirement! I know that you were really looking forward to it, and I enjoyed reading your message. I think that a book is a great project to take on and I look forward to reading it.

It was a pleasure working with you way back in Applications. I too enjoyed the challenges of the SOAs and mini-SOAs. It gave me an appreciation for the breadth of the GE Product Line. I can imagine that today's sessions would be even more impressive with the renewables Products and now the ex-Alstom Steam Plant business.

Again, best wishes and keep in touch.
Regards,
Paul K.

Mike – Congratulations to you!!! You have definitely earned this and I have enjoyed all our time working together and I know you will be missed by many!! It has been such a great time and I know you will continue to do so many wonderful things with your time in retirement and inspire others. I am truly blessed to have known you and worked with you and thank you for all you have done! I hope that we cross paths and keep in touch.

Blessings to you Mike!
Best regards,
Sharon B.

Hello Mike,

I want to wish you well in retirement. I've got mixed feelings about these things— losing a valuable trustworthy colleague but happiness for your pivot into the next phase of life (pivot—GE lingo J). I'll likely join you in retirement a few years from now.

Thank you for all you've done for our company and the discussions, work-outs, etc. we've shared in the past. Your sincerity, trustworthiness, and solid technical and social foundation was always evident to me, and that's what matters most.

> *Good luck and take care,*
> *Larry S.*

It has been a pleasure working with you Mike. You will be missed.

> *Joe P.*

Mike what an awesome email. In the short time I have known you it's been a pleasure. Look forward to seeing you at the retirement dinner (which I hope to have confirmed soon!). Thanks for the shout out, you have been great to work with!

> *Karissa B.*

Congratulations on finally stepping away from work and into retirement. It was a pleasure to work with you on and off over the last four years. I like to think that more has been done to improve the constructability and maintainability of GE equipment in the last 4-5 years than had been done in the 20 years before. Much of that owed to your engagement with the FE50 and other programs, along with the ongoing dialog you fostered between Engineering and Service.

Good Luck on the road ahead, and I hope we bump into each other again sometime.

> *Take Care,*
> *Chris C.*

Congratulations on finishing well in your GE career. I hope I can survive to the end and look back on it as fondly as you!

> *Ben L*

Best wishes for your retirement. It has truly been a pleasure working with you. Enjoy this next phase of your life. I look forward to reading your book when you publish.

> *Ted F.*

Very classy note Mike.
  Gordon S.

Dear all, especially dear Mike!
It has been a privilege to have you on the team, Mike.
Even during this short time, you were able to provide a lot of insights.
You responded to the curious questions of the team of the newly on boarded members to GE coming from Alstom.
You contributed to the integration in an enjoyable open, friendly and constructive way.
Thanks for the insights and experience shared.
As said during our personal meeting last week, I wish you all the best for your retirement phase of life, plenty of hobbies and time for all those things you could not pursue during regular business life.
Enjoy the time with your friend, Joanna, riding the bicycle along Mohawk River and beauty of upstate NY and its colorful seasons.
You have achieved a lot that people will memorize and you simply can be proud of!
Needless to say, (rather young) engineers like me sometimes need a good word of advice to put things into perspective and see things with appropriate wisdom.
Thanks for the details shared below to be able reach out to you. Stay in touch.
Faithfully yours,
  Christian V.

I am moved to see your message and I am honored having worked with you for a brief time even if we never had the opportunity to meet. I would like to thank you for the support and good words.
I like reading history (completing an MSc now) so I will keep an eye for the book, which I will read with interest, and hopefully get it signed by the author. :)
Good luck to the rest of the journey.
  Dimitris K.

The best of luck in your new journey! I will keep you informed of the patent progress.
Best Regards,
  Nestor H.

Congrats Mike! I certainly enjoyed my time working with you and I wish you a very long, happy and prosperous retirement!
    Rex M.

Congratulations Mike, this is a bit of a surprise. You have always been a great co-worker, softball teammate, and friend. I wish you the best of luck in the future!!
    Eric K.

Congratulation on such rich achievements and career. It has been a great pleasure to work with you on [prominent projects], the environmental challenges, and some of the permit testimonies... I DO MISS THOSE DAYS.
    I am sorry with my schedule and availability the last few years, it simply seems that we have no time to spare for fun things any longer. This hopefully will change soon, but I am not holding my breath for it.
    All the best with your retirement... and with your book. Take good care,
    Regards,
      Brahim R.

Congratulations on an incredible 40 years!! I would definitely want to read your book – I look forward to it. Best of luck, and enjoy your well-earned next chapter in life. I'll see you around the fitness center.
    Rich M.

Best wishes for the next chapter of your life. I've enjoyed working with you.
    Bill H.

Congratulations on your retirement! You've earned it and I hope this period of your life is long with great health and happiness.
    Best regards,
      Tom D.

Wishing you all the best with your next chapter in life. Make the most of it.
    Cheers
      -Dale C.
Ps: Your story below was a good read. Thanks for the insights.

It was a pleasure working with you..I can't wait until I retire
Michael S.

Congratulations, Mike! I am very happy for you. What an amazing career you've had. It really was a pleasure working with you. I wish you all the best in this next chapter and hope to cross paths again.
Take care of yourself,
Lori V.

Good luck, and enjoy.
Thanks,
Sal L.

I have enjoyed our professional association. I hope you enjoy retirement.
Best Regards,
Philip A.

Best of luck to you Mike. You are one of the best and will be greatly missed at GE.
Best regards,
John K.

Although I have only known you for a few years it seems like we connected pretty easily and it seems like I have known you longer. I'll have to say, of all of the ongoing / repeating /regularly scheduled conference calls I have been part of.....your calls were some of the more relevant, well run and fruitful discussions we have had. I'll keep you in my contact list and maybe we'll get together once in a while when I'm in Schenectady.
Best of luck to you, Mike, and Congratulations!! We certainly will miss you.
Jeff D.

All the best to you in retirement. It was a pleasure to have worked with you on and off through the years. I wish you all the best and hope that our paths will cross again.
Tony A.

Congratulations! I had no clue next week was your last week! You hired me onto the Merlin team so I have you to thank, or blame :), for my GE career here in Schenectady. I always enjoyed working for you and our conversations after the Merlin years.

I wish you all the best for many many years to come!

Betty B.

PS. I'm soooooooooooooooooo jealous!!!

I'm sad to see you leave but so happy for you and your next chapter. Please stay in touch and I will try to let you know when I am in town so we can have a beer.

Best of luck!

Sue W.

It has been my pleasure to have worked with you. It is amazing what happens and who you meet along the way. I really wish you all the best in your next adventure...

Let me know when the book comes out. I will definitely enjoy the chapter about gas turbine inspection ports

Hope to see you at the fitness Ctr.

Tom B.

Best wishes in your Retirement, Mike! Look forward to owning a copy of your book!

Susan B.

Congratulations! What a great summary of your career. It was a pleasure working with you and sharing a few sporting experiences outside work. I'll never forget the time we accidentally ended up walking through the players and coaches area at one of the Giants open practices.

Scott H.

Best of Luck With Your Retirement and your "To Do List", well deserved after 40 challenging and interesting years.

In reading your reflection summary, I can see you got the best out of GE and GE got the best out of you!

I am glad to have been able to interact with you some during the Empire CSA – GRC dating days.
   Paul T.

I am truly honored to have made the list and wish you all of the best in your years to come.
   Congratulations!!
   Michelle S.

Good luck. It was a pleasure to work with you as well. I look forward to reading your book.
   Best Regards,
   Dave M.

Congratulations!! It was great working with you. You have had a great career, and all your planned activities in retirement will be even better! Enjoy!
   Dave K.

Mike – best of luck. I'd like to read the book when it comes out!
   Kelly F.

Many thanks for your note.
I wish you all the best for the future; let's stay in touch!
All the Best
   Bernard B.

Mike, congrats on starting your new life, so jealous! Enjoy and be good. :)
   -Doug F.

It is an honor to be copied in this email from you.
I truly enjoyed getting to know you and my only regret is that I wish it happened earlier than it did. But I guess later is better than never so I am thankful!
I wish you the best of luck with all the things you plan to do from biking to volunteering and from fixing the house to writing a book. Good luck!!!
If there are plans for a retirement celebration at GE, please let me know if I can be there.

My personal email is: [private]
My cell is: [Private] (GE) and [Private] (personal)
I look forward to staying in touch!
Good luck, Mike!
  Sherif M.

Congrats Mike! All the best!
  John L.

Wow.... 40 years... what an amazing record to wrap up a GE journey. I look forward to seeing you active in the community. Keep in touch!
Here is my personal email [private]
  Meng-Ling H.

Sad to hear that you are leaving us. It has been a pleasure working with you and your team on the projects. I wish you all the best on your retirement and hope that we can keep in touch!
Regards,
  Stephen F.

Wow!!! Boy do I feel old!!! Both you and Terry retiring makes me realize how quickly time has flown by
I saw Lance Hall recently and we shared a laugh over MERLIN/Configurator and thought of the old gang and some of my favorite moments (like replacing George L's service award golf clubs with my daughter's plastic set and having you present those to him).
I wish you all of the best in retirement (you've certainly earned that) and look forward to hearing your tales of great adventures.
Please stay in touch.
  Scott R.

Thanks for the note. Myself, I'm not quite ready as the work I am involved in outweighs the desire to retire.
I wish you the best of luck in you new endeavor and longevity to sustain you for a happy retirement.

You have my e-mail at GE at least for the next few years (Private) or feel free to use my home email [private].

    Best Regards,

      Jim S.

Wow ... 40 years ... that's an accomplishment in and of itself. Congratulations to you ... I can imagine it's bittersweet ... but you deserve break. I appreciate the support and sponsorship you provided me in my early days with Power ... it was key to me getting the visibility that was necessary for progressing my career. It's been a fantastic ride but I do look forward to the "break" someday too. Let's stay in touch. Wish you all the best ... you are definitely one of the "good" guys.

    Cheers,

      Lance H.

Mike, congratulations on the retirement I see mentioned below. It's been a pleasure interfacing with you over the past many years, and I wish you the best in your future endeavors.

    Best Regards,

      Kenny B.

ACKNOWLEDGEMENTS

THANKS TO ALL WHO MADE this book possible, especially my grandparents, parents, so many terrific teachers (formal and informal) and to the co-workers who lived various segments of this story with me.

A VERY HEARTFELT THANKS TO Chris Hunter, VP of Collections at Schenectady's Museum of Industry and Science for his efforts to find valuable family excerpts of my grandparents from older GE News articles.

Special appreciation to Debra Murphy, of 4-Clarity, who did a super job editing and offering some solid advice on my original manuscript. Finally a special thank-you to Joanna Begg whose constant encouragement and editorial suggestions helped me find the correct words and maintain focus, especially when writing some of the more emotional segments.

ABOUT THE AUTHOR

MICHAEL A. DAVI WAS PROFESSIONALLY employed by General Electric for 40 years. His career began and ended with Services Engineering roles and in between there were some most unusual assignments. Often these assignments involved working with top expertise in the company. Gas turbines, primarily industrial power generation equipment, but sometimes including GE aircraft engines, played a prominent role in his career. GE's global power generation business afforded worldwide travel opportunities, exciting work, stellar educational options and great camaraderie with excellent people. Along the way Davi was involved in global technical presentations, project negotiations and environmental regulatory hearings. Membership in the American Society of Mechanical Engineers opened the door to becoming a GE representative and an active committee member on the International Gas Turbine Institute's Electric Power Committee for more than 26 years. Now retired and living in Niskayuna, New York, Davi has written his first book, "PrivileGEd –Experiences From My Unusual 40-year Career With One of America's Most Iconic Companies" to document his story. Hopefully the success he experienced will be an inspiration to younger folks to consider technical careers and perhaps also to others to share their own stories.

To learn more visit: *www.michaeldavi.net* which includes a link to over 100 photos and graphics which illustrate the storyline.

Find him on LinkedIn: *www.linkedin.com/in/michael-davi-95024411*

And follow him on Twitter: *@MDavi_Author*